# THE SHEEP'S TALE

# The Sheep's Tale

*The story of our most
misunderstood farmyard animal*

JOHN LEWIS-STEMPEL

doubleday

TRANSWORLD PUBLISHERS
Penguin Random House, One Embassy Gardens,
8 Viaduct Gardens, London SW11 7BW
www.penguin.co.uk

Transworld is part of the Penguin Random House group of companies
whose addresses can be found at global.penguinrandomhouse.com

Penguin
Random House
UK

First published in Great Britain in 2022 by Doubleday
an imprint of Transworld Publishers

A CIP catalogue record for this book
is available from the British Library.

ISBN 9780857527066

Typeset in 11.5/15pt Granjon LT Std by Jouve (UK), Milton Keynes.
Printed and bound in Great Britain by Clays Ltd, Elcograf S.p.A.

The authorized representative in the EEA is Penguin Random House Ireland,
Morrison Chambers, 32 Nassau Street, Dublin D02 YH68.

Penguin Random House is committed to a sustainable
future for our business, our readers and our planet. This book
is made from Forest Stewardship Council® certified paper.

MIX
Paper from
responsible sources
FSC® C018179

*John Lewis-Stempel with Treacle.*

... our [present] connection with sheep extends no further than driving him to and from his pasture, and that at the expense of much fright and occasional injury, and subjecting him to painful restraint and sad fright when we are depriving him of his fleece.

William Youatt,
*Sheep: Their Breeds, Management and Diseases*, 1837

# CONTENTS

# PROLOGUE

# THE TALE OF ROBIN HOOD

I buried Robin Hood in his favourite place, the little paddock beside the Dulas. Across the brook, somewhere in the hazel thicket that climbed the evening hillside, a blackbird sang requiem.

Maid Marian was there, of course. She was, after all, his number-one wife. I shed no tears; I'd done my crying when the local vet, Peter Jinman, had informed me there was no hope. Robin Hood had irreversible anaemia due to a semi-tropical disease, vectored by a parasitic worm in a bird's dropping. The incomprehensible incongruity of it all was part of the hurt: the Dulas wanders its way in very English Herefordshire.

Even Jinman, a pillar of the veterinary establishment and soon to become president of the Royal College of Veterinary Surgeons, had never encountered *Haemonchus contortus*, barber's pole worm, in Britain.

I wondered on that spring day when we buried Robin if Little John and Friar Tuck would greet him in Heaven. Because surely sheep, of all the creatures, with all that Christian symbolism and parable attached to them, get past St Peter?

*Agnus dei.* 'Behold the Lamb of God, which taketh away the sin of the world.' *John I.29.*

It is twenty years since Robin Hood's interment, but I

remember him, and always with a wry smile. He was a singular ram. A pedigree Ryeland – his official name was Spenwood Xtra Special – he was fat, white, woolly, with a face like a teddy bear; my young children, Tris and Freda, adored him for his cuddliness. I admired his presence, eccentricity, and sheer interest in the world about him. He would sit in that hill-country paddock, its west end framed dramatically by the Black Mountains, on his haunches – *exactly* like a dog – and gaze out through the metal bars of the gate and watch the tractors go past on the lane.

He was a ******, though, when I took in a bale of hay in winter because he would jump up, trying to get first bite from the load on my shoulder. He weighed about 80kg; his methaney breath would be in my face. Any 'sheep cake' (concentrate food) in a bucket and he would be unstoppable, diving in, then wandering off with the blue plastic bucket stuck on his head.

I liked him. And I think he liked me. There were times when he would deign to let me rub him under his chin as he stood four-square, head jutting forward. He was imperious, as if conscious of the glorious history attached to his kind. Ryeland sheep, first bred in the fifteenth century by the monks of Leominster Priory. Robin Hood was not just a sheep in a Welsh Marches paddock. He had ancestry – breeding, you might say.

Neither was he a mindless machine, as the Cartesians used to conceive livestock, his life a blank prelude to being dispatched by the butcher. He had personality. Which is why he had an individual name from us, as well as his state-ordained DEFRA number on his blue ear tag.

I love sheep like Robin. But I admit I sometimes loathe them too.

Which, I think, is pretty much the standard ambivalence of anyone who knows sheep, as I do, having farmed them for twenty-five years. (My family began farming them eight hundred years ago.) When do I hate them? When they *will not* do as you want. When they escape, which they dismayingly do at the most inopportune moment, such as minutes before weddings, funerals, going on that long-promised holiday. Sheep are cunning beyond ken when they set their minds on the greener grass on the other side of the fence, and it always seems to be greener there (to a sheep, at least).

Mostly, I admire sheep, and the more I have 'run them', as we say in Herefordshire, the more they have intrigued me.

This is my laudation to sheep and their place in our lives. And my life in particular. Sheep that have given my life some of its best moments, because few experiences match lambing under spring moonlight, or breaking open a bale of hay in a January snowstorm on the top of a faraway hill, the sheep gathered gratefully around. And you yourself grateful to be their good shepherd.

*Tris and Freda with Action Lamb and May.*

# INTRODUCTION

The sheep have been here almost as long as we have. Although the first Stone Age people to journey into Britain were pure hunter-gatherers, the latter waves brought their semi-domesticated livestock, including sheep, with them. The New Stone Agers spread up the land via the river systems, where the banks acted as natural 'races', or corridors, for the livestock to be driven along; the water floated the Neolithics' coracle-type boats, the animals aboard. Little Noah's Arks.

By the Bronze Age, sheep farming had made irredeemable marks in the landscape. Excavations in the Fens have revealed earthen 'sorting pens' for sheep, and the same Bronze Age people created much of the chalk downlands, and also grassland at previously wooded altitudes. When the Romans colonized in AD 53 they found a landscape very much like that of today – after all, it had been grazed for millennia, with the trees largely gone from the uplands. Those Lake District fells, which have inspired everyone who has ever wandered them lonely as clouds in historic times, were revealed from their arboreal cover by sheep and sheep farmers in prehistory. Grazing over the millennia since has prevented the fells re-wooding, the sheep eating new shoots as they appear.

The Romans, like every other invader, found Britain to be wet, warm (relatively, courtesy of westerlies and the Gulf Stream) and green. In other words, the ideal *terra* for keeping sheep.

Our island story is also the story of our sheep. The proof is there, everywhere you look. Take place-names, even in such an unlikely, über-urban, mega-metropolitan place as London. Woolwich is from the Old English 'wich', a farm that produced wool; Lambeth is the place where lambs were landed; at Shepherd's Bush there was a hawthorn where a sheep herder once took shelter; glitzy Mayfair was the location in the seventeenth century of a springtime sheep and cattle market; the primary elements of Osterley, 'eowstre' + 'leah', record the pasture, or ley, where a flock of ewes was kept. Nearby Lampton was the lamb farm.

Moving outside London: the Old English 'shep' or 'ship' for sheep gives us places as geographically diverse as Shepperton (first recorded in AD 959) in Surrey, Shepton Mallet in Somerset, Shipton in Yorkshire. Wetherby, also in Yorkshire, is where wethers, or castrated male sheep, were kept . . .

Then there is everyday language and folklore. A sheepish smile. As gentle as a lamb. The black sheep of the family. Mutton dressed as lamb. (The Normans, when they invaded, instilled a class division in sheep terminology. The Francophone conquerors gave their nomenclature to the meat of livestock – mutton, beef – which they ate, while the living beast, worked by the enslaved locals, retained its Anglo-Saxon/ Scandinavian terms. 'Lamb' has a Germanic root, meaning 'wee sheep'; in the late Middle Ages, the plural of lamb was, as with ox and child, 'lambren'.)

More common-or-garden sheep terms: like lambs to the slaughter. Be a lamb. Wolf in sheep's clothing. Further, the common phrase 'to separate the sheep from the goats' comes from a passage in the New Testament. In the story, the sheep (righteous people) find salvation with God, and the goats (sinners) are sent to damnation. Red sky at night, shepherd's delight . . .

Shepherds were believed to know the weather. They did (to an extent), because they spent their lives outdoors, watching sheep, gazing at stars, huddling from rain, sheltering from sun, crouching from wind. For centuries almanacs and astrology books were sold on the shepherd's back; in the 1700s the most popular almanac was *The Shepherd of Banbury's Rules to Judge the Changes of Weather* (1744), originally published as *The Shepherd's Legacy* by John Claridge in 1670.

The preface stated:

> The Shepherd, whose sole Business it is to observe what has a Reference to the Flock under his Care, who spends all his Days and many of his Nights in the open Air, and under the wide spread Canopy of Heaven, is in a Manner obliged to take particular Notice of the Alterations of the Weather, and when once he comes to take a Pleasure in making such Observations, it is amazing how great a Progress he makes in them, and to how great a Certainty at last he arrives by mere dint of comparing Signs and Events, and correcting one Remark by another.

The almanacs contained some sense: red skies at night appear when dust and small particles are trapped in the atmosphere by high pressure, and pleasant weather is moving in. The almanacs contained much nonsense. The most notorious weather proverb is 'March comes in like a lion, and goes out like a lamb'. Obviously. March is the month of the spring equinox.

If Britain was ideal for sheep, sheep were ideal for Britain. Sheep were and are extremely effective at extracting energy from natural vegetation, which does not have to be grass. Far from it. My Hebridean sheep – which are of Viking origin – will happily 'browse' bramble, ivy, holly, thistles, wildflowers, as well as 'graze' grass. As a rule, though, the more lush green grass a sheep has access to, the bigger the sheep.

From the beginning, sheep were multi-purpose beasts. They gave milk, wool, meat, skin. Their guts were used for sewing thread, their horns as needles, trumpets and drinking cups. The eighteenth-century agricultural revolution of Jethro Tull is taught in schools; what the textbooks omit is that the first farmyard revolution was in medieval times when sheep were 'folded' on the arable part of southern and Midlands farms to manure them. A sheep is a walking muck-spreader. A living, organic machine for fertilizing ground.

Poor sheep, they never get their due, do they? Let us go back to the late, lamented Robin Hood in a Herefordshire paddock. The humble wool of the back of Ryeland sheep like Robin Hood was the source of medieval England's wealth, stability, power. Democracy. (As Trotsky once pointed out, as soon as you have want, you need a policeman to keep the people in order. Then a policeman, to keep an eye on the policeman . . .) 'Lemster Ore' it was called, from the flocks grazing around Leominster Priory, and worth its weight in gold. Robin Hood was part of our farming history, our national story. His kind, as well as filling the national coffers, filled our stomachs, put the clothes on our backs (and legs, feet, arms, hands, head).

Poor sheep. Overlooked in our history, and now accused of abetting climate change through their 'gaseous emissions' and destroying the landscape with their hooves and mouths. According to zealous rewilders, our mountains are 'sheep-wrecked' when they could be covered bounteously with trees. (The new forests enveloping our uplands will be a sad surprise to curlews, red grouse and skylarks, I suggest.)

*Baa*. Humbug. Sheep can be good for the environment. Back

once more to Robin Hood in his paddock. What he and his merry women were doing was 'conservation grazing', which, by reducing dominant grasses such as ryegrass, allows other grasses and wildflowers to bloom in their millions. With the flowers come the bees and the birds. Robin Hood was *increasing* biodiversity. Sheep farming can be a virtuous circle where we all win: sheep, humans and Nature.

Also, if we get rid of all the sheep from the hills, we get rid of wool. Is that not a sort of madness? The ridding of wool? Wool is sustainable. Natural.

It is odd how little most of us know about sheep, given how deeply entrenched they are in our culture. The Greek astrological sign Aries is a ram. In nursery rhymes, 'Mary had a little lamb', and 'Baa-baa black sheep' was asked if he had any wool. On the screen Shari Lewis's Lamb Chop and Aardman's Shaun the Sheep have gambolled about entertaining families. On Easter cards lambs are no less frolicsome each passing year.

When it comes to sheep, we suffer intentional disconnect, double-think, what psychologists call cognitive dissonance. Those same little lambikins get slaughtered – literally – before they are a year old. On the supermarket shelf they are reduced to abstract, packaged commodities. To cope with this glaring contradiction – Little Gambolling Lamb in Field *v.* Big Rack of Lamb in the Oven – we downplay sheep's intelligence and individuality, hence the traducing expression 'to be a sheep', meaning to be a dumb, passive follower. Even a man as sensitive and attuned to nature as George Orwell made the sheep in *Animal Farm* the stupidest of the stupid, who go from mindlessly chanting 'Four legs good, two legs bad' to 'Two legs good, four legs bad'.

Or we blank the treatment we give sheep. Once upon a time,

sheep were always raised outside in the fresh air, in a system that would, in today's terminology, be called 'extensive', even 'organic'. More than ten million sheep are now stuck in factory farms worldwide; sheep are also used extensively in biomedical research. About twenty-four thousand are used annually for a range of purposes, from the study of Huntington's disease and heart conditions to orthopaedics, organ transplants and genetic research (including cloning). There was a time when sheep were used in Argentina as fuel, their bodies thrown into furnaces. Like logs.

One thing I can tell from twenty-five years of shepherding, starting with two sheep and ending up with one hundred and twenty: sheep are not stupid – except where stupidity has been bred into them by so-called 'improvement' for the convenience of humans. As for sheep being 'sheepish' . . . our sheep have beaten up our dogs.

Sheep are curious things. And sheep farming is a curious old business, where one can become attached to, loving, even, of animals raised for sale, for the pot. That has always been the case. As the Old Testament, which knew a thing or two about shepherding, tells it in *II Samuel*:

> The poor man had nothing, save one little ewe lamb, which he had bought and nourished up: and it grew up together with him, and with his children; it did eat of his meat, and drank of his own cup, and lay in his bosom, was unto him a daughter.

So, my fondness for Robin Hood was not unusual, and I believe spoke of the way we should treat sheep. With respect. That is how sheep farming used to be. And should be again.

Robin Hood was easy to know and like because the species

barrier between sheep and humans is gossamer thin. They are more like us than we may care to know. Sheep form friendship bonds, as well as family and flock ones.

I have made mistakes over the last twenty-five years, some terrible. I once had to put an injured sheep out of its misery. I did so in the corner of a field, but still in view of the flock. After the blast from the Lincoln 12-bore shotgun, the sheep changed their relationship with me. No longer was I the nice guy who gave them food; I was the killer. Far from crowding around me on my arrival in the field, they kept up the safety distance of wild animals. Our relationship had gone bust. It took months to heal, because sheep remember.

I understand the ethical objection to sending a lamb to the abattoir. (I don't like the process either, and don't do it any more.) In the good old days, a sheep would be raised to productive adulthood and only eaten when this time had expired, which was about the length of its natural life: five to seven years.

I like sheep, on the plate and on the hill. It *is* possible to have your sheep and eat it. To have happy meat. It all depends on how the sheep are farmed.

∼

After writing the above words, I put down the laptop lid and walked up the farm track to check the Ryeland sheep in the top, lane-side field.

They were grazing up the hill; on the skyline they made white clouds among the white clouds of the September morning. (Sheep tend to have two primary grazing periods, during the early morning and again late in the afternoon.) A starling hopped off and on to the back of a ewe called Valentine, in the manifestation of an ancient symbiotic alliance: the starling picks off insects (food), the sheep is de-pested. Hence the local names of 'sheep stare' and 'shepstarling'.

I like being outside with the sheep, tending them, watching Nature. This is my life.

The sheep were in a good mood, and so was I. Standing there, watching them eat and utter the occasional *baa* to connect with each other, a wild thought came into my head, and would not leave. (Counting sheep might induce somnia; observing them induces reflection.) Sheep were the first domesticated farmyard animal. But perhaps the process of taming them actually tamed us?

# JOHNNY HAD A LITTLE LAMB
# (OR TWO THOUSAND)

### YOUNG LAMBS

*The spring is coming by a many signs;*
*The trays are up, the hedges broken down,*
*That fenced the haystack, and the remnant shines*
*Like some old antique fragment weathered brown.*
*And where suns peep, in every sheltered place,*
*The little early buttercups unfold*
*A glittering star or two – till many trace*
*The edges of the blackthorn clumps in gold.*
*And then a little lamb bolts up behind*
*The hill and wags his tail to meet the yoe,*
*And then another, sheltered from the wind,*
*Lies all his length as dead – and lets me go*
*Close bye and never stirs but baking lies,*
*With legs stretched out as though he could not rise.*

JOHN CLARE

Snow, and the sort of snow that denies physics. Snow that falls, but only to swoop up to collect under the chin, under the brim of a cap.

Snow, and the sort of snow that confirms meteorology. Snow that turns the blue air of a March, spring-promising morning white.

People wish for snow at Christmas, but in my lifetime there have been more pale Easters than white Noels. So, no change there for English country folk. In 1820 John Clare observed in 'The Shepherd's Calendar':

*March month of 'many weathers' wildly comes*
*In hail and snow and rain and threatning hums*

In the UK, according to the Met Office, snow or sleet falls on average 3.9 days in December and 4.2 days in March. The Great Blizzard of 1891 came on 9 March and caused drifts twenty feet high in the West Country.

March's snow is harsh and hissing. Unsoft. Cruel. The lexicon of the Inuit contains fifty finely graded words for snow. I have only one word for this day's English snow, and it is unprintable.

Between the hurls of false blossom, a landscape glimpsed. Below me, old, gnarly apple orchards of the sort you get in Herefordshire, and the dull pencil line of the Wye. Horizontally, across my sight, a flint arrowhead flies: a kestrel on some pitiless raptorial mission.

And yet, this is winter's last grasp of the talons. The signs of spring cannot be obliterated. Yesterday, a peacock butterfly batted about the ivied copse, in the same bemused way tourists wander Inca ruins in the jungle. The peacock was joined in the dancing air by a brimstone, as bright yellow as butter and the reason that lepidoptera are called 'butterflies'. A woodpecker drummed somewhere across the valley with pure joie de vivre, and on the garden path were earthworms, lost and mapless in their spring dispersal. Primroses burst on the bank, scenting the sweet scene, and above them, on the tip of the oak's scaffold, the song thrush sang its mating song, cocky and croony: 'Get-up-get-up-get-up; come-along-run-along'.

The signs of spring are irrefutable down on the farm, as well as in Nature. There is earth on the plough blades, from the drilling of barley. The haystack in the barn has had the heart eaten out of it. And there are lambs about.

My friend said, 'I've got a wedding. Could you pop in and check the sheep around lunchtime? Should all be OK, we're not due to begin lambing till next week . . .'

The ellipsis was eloquent.

My friend has twenty Jacob sheep, piebald and primitive. Parkland sheep that bring a bit of class with them, as well as making a bit of money.

Counting sheep is only easy in bed. In a domey, tussocky field in hill country, in snow, with white-and-black sheep keeping a wary distance, it is testing. I count nineteen sheep. Then twenty. Then nineteen again.

Occasionally, the sheep shake the snow from their fleeces, and blur. The ram, four-horned and magnificent, moves to put himself pridefully and protectively between me and the flock. With his snow beard, he could pass as a patriarch from the Old Testament. Which, in a way, he is. According to the Book of Genesis, Jacob took 'every speckled and spotted sheep' from his father-in-law Laban. Hence 'Jacobs'. Gene science backs the Bible; Jacob sheep display a homogenous R2 retrotype different from the other British ovine populations and akin to Asiatic and African breeds.

How the cloven hooves of Jacob sheep came to walk on England's pleasant pastures green is a mystery. Truly, God only knows.

A Jacob ram in flock-guard mode is to be treated with respect. This I do know, because we used to keep Jacobs, and dear Rameses once smashed two fingers of my hand with one butt of his head. Jacobs were the first sheep we ever had, two of them, Bledwynn and One Puppy, bought from a farm in the Cotswolds, and brought home in the back of the Land Rover, the four of us – myself, my wife Penny, and the two children, Tris and Freda – crammed in the front.

Some sheep names one gives; some are inherited. 'One Puppy' was named by the seller for her habit of springing a single lamb. We were once donated a Hebridean ram called . . . 'Rammy'.

I've digressed. On this morning, on this hill, I back off, and count the flock once more. Nineteen.

I find the missing ewe down the bank, in a long shallow hull of a ditch where a hedge used to be. She is prone; at her head a crown of roots from an upturned hawthorn. There is snow on her flank, and a gargoyle protruding from under her tail.

Jacobs usually birth with ease, but in every flock there is one. The ewe is young, a first-timer, and in her eye there is fear when she raises her head to look at me. Something else too: that special helplessness and innocence of sheep that make them a Christian symbol.

Thanks to my friend's sufficient silence on the phone, I have the key bits of lambing kit packed about my coat. So out with the disposable gloves and the pink lubricant gel.

In the slush and the urine of the snowy hollow I lie down

and push the head of the lamb back inside the ewe's fleshy birth canal, followed gently by my fingers. (Like every cold shepherd ever, I think at this point, 'Nice and warm in here, at least.') A relief, for me and for her: no great difficulty to sort the puzzle. The lamb's front legs are bent under the body, rather than in the requisite dive position.

The wind and the snow blow through the rusty barbed wire fence next to us.

Fiddle about, align and pull. With the veterinary gel and birth slime, this is as easy as grabbing a jellied eel, but the little ewe pushes too.

A yolky alien pod is emitted. I rub it, blow up its nose. Is the lamb alive?

A tremble in its chest. I put the lamb to the mother's head. In her too the will to live comes. Ewe and lamb convulse alike, electric-shock-started. The ewe gets to her feet, begins licking the lamb. The lamb does a perceptible shake of the head. Then a snuffle. In dialect, the lamb is 'sharp' – vital. Within minutes my little lamb is up on its preposterous stilts.

Risen.

I see now that the ewe had been lying against unfurled buttercups. The snow did not reach them.

~

Left to its own devices a northern hemisphere ewe, such as the Jacob, will 'lamb' in March. It is a simple matter of biology synchronizing with botany. March is the month of the spring equinox, improving weather, and crucially the temperature of the earth remains more or less constantly above 6 degrees so that grass – the sheep's staple food – grows, meaning that both ewe and the newborn lamb can eat.

The ewe, along with other mammals, is able to regulate, to an extent, the exact day of birth so as to take advantage of the weather. Dry days are best, because nothing kills lambs so efficiently as rain. Plastic 'foul weather' jackets, squares with four leg holes, are always a key part of the lambing kit of the human midwife; once, when these were unobtainable, I wrapped the lambs in plastic carrier bags from Sainsburys, an ironic statement of their end destination.

Farmers make much brouhaha over the trials of lambing, but this is self-imposed travail. Hill and primitive ewes invariably lamb quickly and cleanly, because of genetics: failures died. It is Darwin's natural selection up on the farm. Modern sheep breeds tend to lamb less easily than traditional ones, because farmers artificially manipulate diet and genetics to get heavy twin lambs ('doubles'), or even triplets. Ewes, though, have just two teats. Improved sheep are generally also less hardy.

A gambolling lamb and Easter used to be synonymous; the ovine infant and the Lamb of God both arose into life in spring. Nowadays, in order to get a market edge, there are farmers who lamb their sheep every eight months – as opposed to every twelve – under 'accelerated lambing' programmes requiring artificial darkness. In other words, these 'shepherds' are working against nature, and not with it.

Sheep of the old breeds do more than select the sensible month to give birth, they pick the time of day, a six-hour delivery slot between midnight and dawn, meaning that the newborn lamb will be warmed by daylight, not chilled by evening's gloom. The lee of the hedge is a favourite maternity spot, although we also provide our pregnant ewes with some fetching strawbale 'houses' with corrugated iron roofs. The ewe about to lamb is easy to spot: her udder fills up and stiffens, she gets uneasy and goes off on her own, she begins to stretch upwards to gaze at the sky, maybe scrape a bit of hollow, and lies down. Absolute imminence of birth is the emergence of the saggy 'water bag' from the vulva.

But sheep being sheep, there are the wilful exceptions to the ovine norm. For a decade Tiddlywink, a katmoget Shetland, insisted on lambing in the middle of the field, on a hillside, in the rain, at random hours, and every time she made a hash of it, meaning I spent more time with my gelled hand inside her womb than any other sheep's in a quarter of a century. The lambs were invariably breeched, and in my more exasperated moments, lying on my side, drenched by rain and night, at about 10 p.m., I would mutter the 'A' word (abattoir). The gaudy string of lights, red and blue and yellow and green, above the door of the Crown, the village pub way, way down the dark valley, always tantalized beyond her head.

On one occasion, when she was losing strength and I was losing patience, I called out the vet from south Hereford (Jinman having retired from farm work), whose pearl of wisdom was to suggest she was fed more concentrate food.

Tiddlywink? The sheep that wouldn't go near a trough, or indeed anything human?

I suspect the reason we persevered with Tiddlywink over the years (she was twelve when she died) was that she was the most exquisite of sheep: fawn-coloured with black face-stripes, hence the Gaelic *katmoget*, badger-like. An oddity of sheep is the inverse relationship between aesthetics and maternalism. The more beautiful the ewe, it seems, the worse her mothering.

Her children – named Tiddlywink II, Tiddlywink III etc; there are times when one runs dry on lamby names – continued her line of beauty, their births little miracles, an absolute defying of science whereby a newborn creature unfolds long, ridiculously tottery legs and stands within minutes, even seconds.

Unfair, of course, that one tends to remember the difficult births best. The hundreds of ewes who got the lambs out aidlessly are less securely fixed in memory, unless they produced curiosities. Or just kept going, beating the biological clock. Such as Sooty.

Sooty the Shetland was an accidental purchase from Ross-on-Wye livestock market, on the roundabout, next to Labels, the cut-price fashion store. There was a special sale of pedigree sheep, and I'd gone with my son, Tris, then five, to 'do a bit of research'. Just that. We ran Jacobs at the time, both the two-horned and four-horned varieties, for their wool (useful to hand-spinners), for meat (so-so success), as living adornments (very successfully) for landowners. But Sooty, in a pen of metal hurdles, her papers sellotaped to the bars, entranced me. She was a 'Juglet' Shetland, meaning she had Panda-patch eyes on a black and white colour scheme; indeed, from a distance she mirrored a collie.

She was so finely boned, so exquisite. I kept returning to her pen, eyeing suspiciously anybody who paid her more than passing interest. I pretended no interest at all, a passing glance was all she got from me. (Livestock markets are all about playing mental games.) So I stood in the crowd as the auctioneer began moving along the pens. At Sooty's pen, he commenced his 'Do I hear?' spiel, and I raised my hand, immediately. All guile gone. £5. One other bidder . . . seen off for £7.

This is how auctions go. One thinks, 'Why stop at buying the one object?' – in this case sheep. One soon concludes, 'Silly not to have another. Keep her company.'

Next Shetland along, held in her pen by the seller on a rope. The Shetland ewe is fawn. I'd noticed her: nice fleece, plenty of lustre, certificate for 'Prize-Winning Wool' attached to the top of the pen. Sure enough, bidding starts at £5 . . . lots of interest. The auctioneer, in tweed, stood on a box, selling goods rather than God. 'Do I hear £8, £9 . . .'

Plenty of bidders. She is a good sheep. OK 'conformity', even if the eyes are a bit protruding, like a Creature Comfort animal, but that fleece . . . Are the other bidders genuine, or accomplices of the seller pushing the bidding up? (It has been known.)

Two bidders left standing. A woman with a ledger, pages of notes, about five seats along. And me.

I get the ewe for £15.

I came to look. I now have two sheep. Maybe we should have a small flock of Shetlands?

Thus it is that Tris and I go home in the Land Rover with five Shetland ewes, of several colours, in the back. Baaing.

This was October 1999, and you could just put sheep in the back of the Land Rover then, without forms in triplicate. Of these starter five, Sooty was the leader, the dominant sheep, although she was the youngest – she was a 'shearling' ewe, meaning she had been shorn once, and had not yet lambed.

Sooty went to the tup, a Jacob, in November, and produced, in the spring of 2000, a Juglet ewe lamb. Sooty lived for fifteen years. She produced with a flourish a single black-and-white lamb each year as regular as spring. She lambed in the last year of her life, and due to her age, I decided to sit with her during labour. Just in case.

It was a March night to remember. The moon had a giant glowing ring around it – a moon halo, caused by the moonlight refracting through ice crystals. (Yes, you can still get miracles.) At about 4 a.m. Sooty lambed under the moonlight, emitting a slimy plasticky package. There is nothing uglier than a newborn lamb.

Sooty was mute throughout, because sheep are prey animals and try for silence when weak. A tawny owl kept shrieking from the wood; I was shivering, despite the multiple gilets and coats that made me look like the Michelin man's fat brother. Sooty did her usual magnificent maternal routine. Licked the lamb. Licked it, licked again. First the membrane off the face, then the lamb's body with her tongue to stimulate it into life. The lamb was a black-and-white patchwork, because it was one of those magical times when the designs of Nature are perfectly coordinated. The black-and-white lamb was born under a willow tree, in plots of dark and moonlight. Within minutes the lamb was standing; uncertain, bemused, but standing. Would the tottery lamb find the teats? The lamb headbutted all the wrong places ... Then latched on. The tiny tail wagged happily.

The lamb was beautiful. Because nothing is prettier, gentler-eyed than a new lamb. When the lamb had suckled, I picked it up and sprayed the navel in an antiseptic, gentian violet, to prevent joint ill. In my hands, I could feel the silken curls of her fleece. A girl. She was kept and she was called Moonlight.

All our sheep have names, the names a rough-hand mnemonic to colour, type, date of birth, or an imagined resemblance to a character, real or fictional, or to a personality trait: Chocolate, Sooty, Soo, Tiddlywink, Shortbread, Cardigan, Jumper (of course), Valentine, Tess ... You come to live with us, you get a name.

My eyes were teary, but only, of course, because of the cold. Sooty – protective, annoyed – stamped her feet. I returned the lamb to her and she led it away across the paddock to join some shearlings. They became shadows on the frost. Black. White.

~

The lamb's suckling causes the mother's womb to contract and expel the placenta, which she may eat, and if she does not do so some waiting wildlife will. The afterbirth is red and purple; a pearlescent, fleshy puddle. It is prized by red kites, foxes, badgers, stoats, buzzards. On one memorable day a rat in broad daylight sat on its haunches in the grass, its front hands pushing afterbirth into its mouth; on a more memorable day still, when the field up to the lane was perfect with snow icing, two crows were pulling at a stringy length of placenta, their heads red and bloody. They moved left and right, along and around, the placenta pulled between their beaks, in a quadrille.

~

Sheep were the first 'meat animal' to be domesticated. This was during a generously conceived archaeological period between 9,000 and 8,000 BC. The place, however, was more specific: the Fertile Crescent (today's western Iran and Turkey, and all of Syria and Iraq).

Domestication was not a linear process, a steady line of progress. Indeed, sheep (*Ovis aries*) were probably domesticated at least three separate times in the Fertile Crescent, and domestication involved three different subspecies of the wild mouflon (*Ovis gmelini*). Prior to DNA and mtDNA studies, other species (urial, argali) were hypothesized as the ancestor of modern sheep; it is not the case. Sheep come from mouflon.

Mouflon were wild but had several characteristics, notably a relative lack of aggression, manageable size, and early and high reproduction rates, which made them especially suitable for domestication. In the process, sheep changed shape. There was a reduction in body size, female sheep became de-horned ('polled'). The heart shrunk, as did the brain (by about 20 per cent) and the eye sockets, and the tendency to moult disappeared. Sheep went from predominantly dull brown to predominantly off-white. (There is much we still do not understand about sheep – white sheep will become ill from eating buckwheat, whereas dark-woolled sheep do not.)

From the Fertile Crescent, *Ovis aries* dispersed across Eurasia and Africa. Via migratory episodes (of accompanying humans), sheep reached Britain with Neolithic settlers around 4000 BC and these were small, brown, horned sheep, similar to present-day Soays from Scotland. (Preserved wool from the Bronze Age appears to be Soay.) Other living relics of the first ovine migrations are Hebrideans, Shetlands and others from 'Viking' or Nordic short-tailed sheep which, by an idiosyncrasy of nature, have only thirteen vertebrae in their tails, compared to twenty in other sheep. The origins of most modern British breeds are from a later migration, from the Near East into southern Britain.

Something of the domestication process of sheep is clear from the excavated ruins of the ancient Turkish village of Aşıklı Höyük, by the Melendiz river. There are large walls; inside these four walls layers of sheep dung. Thus, the behaviourally wild sheep were penned. Penning enabled villagers to select less aggressive animals over the generations.

A hypothesis: a child in the village took an orphan lamb as a pet, cared for it.

Think about that. To domesticate the sheep required considerable cooperation and forethought by the villagers. Additionally, the long-term taming of the sheep required sensitivity, and responsibility too. You cannot tame sheep by fear.

The purpose of domestication was meat. As the wild mouflon was declining in numbers, farming them was a clever way of managing a dwindling resource. The accidental, useful by-products of ovine domestication were milk, horn, bone, dung, and a hide to be tanned and worn as a kind of tunic. Wool came later, about 3000 BC. Quite possibly, the development of sheep-skin clothing and wool clothing encouraged humans to live in areas far colder than the Fertile Crescent, where temperatures averaged 70°F (21°C). Sheep, in other words, may have helped spread civilization northwards.

~

Shepherds are generally greater readers than other types of farmer, not least because during the long overnight hours of lambing you cannot get to sleep and you need to fill the time (and counting sheep is already the thing you are doing). Since no farmer likes to see time wasted, the reading matter will be a man-ual. About tractors. About livestock housing. Or about livestock themselves. I was introduced to William Youatt's *Sheep, their Breeds, Management, and Diseases, to which is added the Mountain Shepherd's Manual*, in 1997 or thereabouts, on top of Cwm Hill, chatting from the window of my Land Rover to Lindsay Lloyd passing down the 'pitch' in his. 'Youatt's still the best,' he declared, regarding the multifarious manuals aimed at the novice shep-herd. He pronounced 'Youatt' as 'Yowt' so it took me a while on my first and brand new PC, a Dan, via the Alta Vista search engine, to find 'William Youatt', English veterinary surgeon.

To my slight surprise, Lindsay Lloyd's recommended mas-terwork was written in 1837. Anyway, since we then lived only fourteen miles from Hay-on-Wye, 'town of books', obtaining a copy (from the Cinema Bookshop) was a piece of Welsh cake.

Son of a conformist minister, Youatt (1776–1847) was edu-cated for the nonconformist ministry, and undertook ministerial and scholastic duties in London. At an unknown date, he joined Delabere Pritchett Blaine at a veterinary practice near Oxford Street in London. In 1828 Youatt began to deliver lectures and demonstrations to veterinary students at his private infirmary in Nassau Street, and later at University College London. In 1835 he was appointed as the Honorary Veterinarian Surgeon of the new Society for the Prevention of Cruelty to Animals (given a Royal Charter in 1840). Something of his enlightened approach to animal care was signalled by his 1839 book, *The Obligation and Extent of Humanity to Brutes*. He was an original member of the Royal Agricultural Society of England (founded in 1838). Youatt's many works include: *Canine Madness*, 1830; *The Horse*, 1831; *Cattle, their Breeds, Management, and Diseases*, 1834; *The Dog*, 1845, and *The Pig: a Treatise on the Breeds, Management, Feeding, and Medical Treatment of Swine; with Directions for salting Pork and curing Bacon and Hams*, 1847.

But it is *Sheep, their Breeds, Management, and Diseases, to which is added the Mountain Shepherd's Manual*, first published by Baldwin and Cradock in London, that has stood the test of time. Quite a time, indeed, from 1837 to now – nearly two centuries. The book, of course, is helped by the simple fact that hill-shepherding is almost timeless. Nearly eternal.

∼

Lambing paddock, lit by mother-of-pearl moonshine. The sheep spread out, in little constellations.

Music of brook. Chorus of sheep.

Lambs popping out like corks.

At some point in the yearly lambing comes into my head, inevitably, 'Shepherds watched their flocks by night . . .'

I am seated on the ground, leaning against one of the

strawbale shelters, in full kit: boots, waterproof trousers, the Barbour slick with wax, even slicker with accumulated coating of lanolin from the years of handling sheep.

Trying to work out how many lambs I have 'midhusbanded' in adulthood: 1,866, 1,881, 1,887, 1881 . . .

I fall asleep. Am awoken by my pockets being rifled. I am being robbed by moonlight.

Action Ram (né Action Lamb, but renamed in his sexual maturity for his unfeasibly large bollocks and appetite for 'covering' any ovine, male or female) has his big Suffolk camelid nose in a side pocket, seeking treats. He has a sweet tooth. I see he has turned over the lambing kit toolbox on a hunt for glucose. For once, thankfully, I've remembered to fasten the catch. Earlier in the night, I put down on the grass a bottle of milk for a lamb. Action Ram grabbed it, sucked at the teat. A giant baby.

An orphan, he was brought up on the bottle himself, years ago.

~

The glucose is for those lambs struggling for life. Glucose is energy is heat. You get cold lambs warm from the inside, as well as the outside. In extremis, you wang it into them, down the throat or by injection into the stomach.

Sometimes I bang it into myself in coffee. *Zing!* The house is only a hundred yards away; sometimes it may as well be a hundred miles. The tiredness drags one into slow motion, turns the skin grey.

But I am euphoric. I love these lambing nights: just me, the sheep, the stars, the dark, and the life-affirming lambs. The night belongs to us, and to hope.

~

The lambing paddock, about three acres, is below the brow of the hill, so the west winds and rains of Wales are partially blocked. Aside from my fabricated strawbale shelters, there is a long line of hawthorn and blackthorn trees on the north-west. According to taste and experience, the ewes select their lambing positions, under the hedge or by the straw. Dear gentle old Sooty is a strawbale girl, and likes other ewes around her. This year she delivered a single piebald ram lamb (Pierrot).

All good, except putting the castrating ring on Pierrot. I forget for a day, then have to divert Sooty with food, while I make a grab for the lamb. It might only be a day old, but it is nimble and quick. I could try to pen, but that is extra time, and extra effort. So I do the traditional shepherd's lunge: full-length rugby tackle and catch the lamb by the back legs.

I love the feel of lambs (after they have been dried off). The tight, ridgy astrakhan coat, the warm ripply muscle underneath.

~

Fog, as soft and enveloping as fleece. Chocolate has wandered over to lamb alone and in private under the hedge, as is her wont.

There is a nudge at my leg. Robin Hood wanting a rub. Or maybe to remind me to cast my eyes over his ewes on the house side of the paddock. I turn on the 2-million-candle-watt torch; reflected off the fog, the light is blinding. So I walk over on auto-pilot. The Ryeland ewes are all flat out, sleeping. 'Not yet,' I say to Robin.

I look at the Ryeland ewes, white and fat with fecundity. Replete with contentment.

Contentment is a transmissible condition. I catch it off the sheep.

~

The old-time shepherds used to sleep with their sheep, out in the fields. I do it sometimes too, on the dry nights, the sheep lying down around me. I'm not sure on those nights who is protecting whom.

~

All the birds stop their singing. The hen sparrow on the ledge turns to stone; an instant ornament. Beyond the window the entire world goes to stillness and gloom. And cold; I can feel the temperature drop. Even through the glass.

Only one local bird of prey produces such petrification. There it is, the red kite with its five-and-a-half-foot wingspan. A travelling mini eclipse.

I carry on filling in the DEFRA Holding Register (half of farming is paperwork), and wait for the dawn chorus to restart.

But the next sound to come to the window is rapid bleating: the distress call of a ewe.

I would like to claim I Usain-Bolted all the way to the lambing paddock, but wellingtons and gathered years restrict me to a British gallop, over the lawn, through the gate.

There is, I suppose, a magnificent insolence to the red kite, perched like a trophy hunter on the black astrakhan corpse of the lamb. The kite tears away dementedly; the grey face feathers become blooded to the crown. The kite's etiquette is ripping off flesh.

I am almost on the bird before it flaps away low and lazy over the blackthorn hedge, clotted with March blossom, towards the mountains of Wales. The sun is on the kite's back and it twists, as if wanting to bathe its whole being in the golden rays.

I look down at the lamb. Curious how natural-born avian carnivores go for the body parts humans despise, such as the soft guts. People aver that red kites never kill lambs. But I am not so sure. The lamb had been wobbling around on new legs minutes before, and a Hebridean lamb can be no bigger than a rabbit. So for me the jury remains out on whether kites kill lambs, but, then, who can blame them? It is the natural order.

Certainly, lambs are meat-magnets for confirmed killers galore. Buzzards. Foxes. Badgers. Ravens. And if you ever want to witness the Mr Hyde inside a horse, show it a baby ovine. Once, our Shetland pony broke into a lamb pen and killed two by biting them on the neck and flinging them into far space.

There is an old country saying that you can tell when spring has come because you can cover five daisies with your foot. An alternative indicator, I see, is that the cadaver of a Suffolk X Hebridean lamb encompasses twenty daisies. The sward is in full 'flush', brought about by the magic number of 6°C. The lambs eat the verdant emergent grass; we and other carnivores eat the lambs.

～

The fox is an apex predator. And apex predators take any convenient beast. In hilly west Herefordshire, where England laps the border of Wales, we've had lambs killed by foxes. The teeth marks on the back of the neck, the nip of the spinal cord, are the forensic reproof of the guilty party. To be balanced on the farm books, though, is the number of rabbits a fox eats, leaving the den entrance beneath the oak ankle-deep in lapine pelts. Seven rabbits eat as much grass as one sheep. The Burns

Inquiry, a government committee set up in 1999 to examine all the issues around the debate on hunting foxes with hounds, surmised that less than 2 per cent of healthy lambs are killed by foxes in England and Wales, but remarked that 'levels of predation can be highly variable between farms and between different areas'. In the lowlands, lambs are frequently kept indoors. As many as 96 per cent of Welsh livestock farmers, according to a 2013 survey, had suffered financially as a result of foxes killing their lambs. Mountain farmers – and Wales is largely mountainous – tend to have smaller breeds of sheep, with resultant smaller lambs. The fresh-born lamb of a mountain breed is frequently no bigger than a rabbit. My own personal anecdotal evidence is that foxes take lambs in particularly pluvial times. No animal wants to hunt in endless rain.

~

According to William Youatt, at lambing time:

The lamber should have with him his lamb-crook; a bottle of milk – ewe's milk if possible, and carried in his bosom or in an inside pocket, that it may be kept warm; some cords to tie legs of the ewes that he may have occasion to assist or to examine; a little pot of tar, with two or three small marking-irons, that he may place a different mark on each pair of twins, in order that he may be enabled afterward to recognise them; another little pot of grease or oil, to lubricate his hand, if he should have occasion to introduce it into the womb of any of the ewes; a sharp knife, with a round or rather curved extremity, should it be necessary to remove the lamb piecemeal from the mother; a piece of stout polished iron rod, of the size of a goose-quill, twelve inches in length, and rounded at one end, somewhat like a button-hook, in order to remove from the womb a dead or divided foetus; a sheep's drenching-horn; a small bottle of cordial, consisting of equal parts of brandy and sweet spirit of nitie; and a strong infusion of ergot of rye. If the ochre had been applied to the ram, and the order in which those ewes were stained by it had been noted, he would be aware what ewes required the earliest watching. This is seemingly a trifling thing, yet it may be the cause of many a lamb being saved in the course of the season. As he goes his rounds among them he should raise every ewe that appears early in the list, and which he finds lying down, and he should observe whether there are about her any symptoms of approaching labor; and as the ewe-flock had previously been kept as free from disturbance as possible, he should now approach them with additional care and tenderness. In the more open parts of the country, the ewes, as the lambing time approaches, should be folded every night. With commendable humanity, and prudence too, the hurdles are frequently guarded with straw. Mr. Price says that he knew a grazier who used boarded hurdles as a protection to the lambs, and they were lambed in folds, the lamber attending on them during the night. When he lived in Herefordshire the ewes were driven into cots every night during the lambing. They were turned out in the day into an adjoining pasture, and had peas and straw . . .

My modern lambing kit, toted in one of those plastic DIY toolboxes: colostrum powder, bottle, rubber tube (to insert down throat of lambs needing a colostrum boost), veterinary lubricant gel, glucose, warm water (in thermos), latex disposable gloves, cheese wire to dismember dead lamb, thin lambing rope (to extract recalcitrant lambs), purple spray (gentian violet), foul weather jackets (failing those, carrier bags and parcel tape). Rubber castration rings and pliers to apply them. Ear tags and the pliers to apply them, like ear-piercing for humans, but with ID and for life. We do not 'fold' (pen) our lambs, but time has taught me to place strawbale shelters facing south, and in the middle of the paddock, not near human noise or the paddock ends, where any predator might lurk.

I do have a shepherd's crook, aluminium, the shorter version, much the length of a walking stick. It might be composed of twentieth-century alloy rather than wood, but it is still, unmistakably, a crook, with a curved head to catch a sheep by the neck or back leg, or the 'handlebars' on a horned breed. Or to recover a fallen animal. For this reason the crook has been used as a religious symbol of care, including the Christian bishop's crozier.

I use the crook for driving the sheep; it acts like a giant arm. Also for beating back bramble thickets to rescue those sheep who insist on getting tangled in the stuff, and for pulling out of the brook those who fall in. Once, I got frostbite in my feet from the March nights outside on the hill under the Black Mountains, then some farm organism entered the affected skin. My foot swelled, started turning black. So I went off to my GP at Ewyas Harold. Dr Whissler prescribed antibiotics. About ten minutes after I got home the phone rang. It was Dr Whissler: 'On second thoughts, I think you should go to hospital . . .'

Two hours later at Hereford County Hospital, where I was born and my daughter Freda was born, the consultant was drawing a dotted line across my instep. 'If the sepsis proceeds past here, we'll have to amputate your foot . . .'

In an English effort to be jolly, keep up a stiff upper lip, I replied, 'Well, it would make buying shoes cheaper . . .'

Fortunately, pumping me with antibiotics for a week, from

a syringe the size of a bicycle pump, cured me. But I hobbled for weeks after. I leant on my shepherd's crook.

Leaning on a crook on the hillside, casting your eye over the sheep as they safely graze, you feel part of tradition.

~

Lambing comes in only two ways: swimmingly well, or drowningly bad. When the newborn lambs do not raise their heads and bleat . . . a blurred flurry of rubbing, air blown up noses. Turn the ewe over, tweak at her teats to break the black wax cap. Pull on her teats to make sure colostrum is running, put the lamb on teat. No colostrum running. Red stomach tube to deliver bought-in colostrum from Wynnstays. Glucose. Purple spray on hanging navels. After the first year or so, you can do it on automatic.

With the lambs that are born dead, or die within hours, I still grieve with closed eyes for the life never lived. There truly is nothing so innocent as a newborn lamb. But I do not grieve as much as their mothers. Some ewes will stand over the dead lamb, calling it, as though words could make it rise. When their dead lambs are taken away (as they must be, by law) they will keep returning to the spot where they last saw their lamb. And cry, and cry. They mirror human mothers.

Only about 5 per cent of our primitive ewes have ever needed help in labour. Shetland and Hebridean ewes birth with a feral ease, the curly black lambs vital, up and walking within minutes. No, the wearing habit of primitive sheep is not their birthing technique, it is the flightiness of the mother ewes. Such as when something comes visiting the lambing paddocks at night, sending the sheep into a baaing delirium.

~

I am out with a torch. The intruder in the paddock is gone. One Hebridean ewe, who has just lambed, runs off, leaving her twins behind. Over the course of this greasy grey day I try to reconnect her with her offspring, finally resorting to catching her and penning her so tight she cannot turn, and then putting the lambs in to suckle. All she does is jump up and down on them; before they are murdered, I let her go, and put them on the bottle. They live in the sitting room in a dog-crate. Sheep tamed by being bottle-fed are no bad thing, since it means they will, when grown, come to food, even to call. And the rest of the flock will follow.

~

I concede that it is unusual to keep lambs in the sitting room. Traditionally, the bottle-fed lambs, for their first days, are kept in the farm kitchen. (My grandfather, who farmed hops for most of his life, detoured into sheep during the Second World War. He revived hypothermic orphan lambs by placing them in the warming oven of the Aga.)

The sitting room has its uses, and facilities, however. There is a log fire, a steady passage of people and dogs (both constituting company), plus the JVC sound system and the TV. And my favourite armchair, spacious and deep, stuffed with horse hair and inherited from my mother-in-law. During lambing, I throw some old sheets over the chair to protect the cotton fabric from my sheep-stunk Dickies boiler suit (essentially a romper suit for adults), and sit there bottle-feeding the orphans on my lap, lamb 'cutched' in left arm, bottle in right hand (somewhat tilted), most of the lights off. Quite often I put a disc in the sound system: the Royal Philharmonic playing Bach's aria 'Where Sheep May Safely Graze'.

This scene is this year, the year before, every year. I do not watch TV. The TV is for the orphan lambs when they get bored and no one is around. Obviously I ensure that a cookery show is not on.

A lamb on the lap, feeding it with a bottle, is simultaneously the most elemental and most high form of shepherding. Sucking on the life-milk through the rubber teat, the lamb enters a state of bliss, as do I. I am doing my job of animal husbandry successfully. The oxytocin courses in both directions.

Orphan lambs, before they can be taught to self-serve, require feeding every four hours. Going to bed is pointless, so I sleep in the chair too.

Volac's Lamlac ewe-milk replacer is not just for sheep. The great advantage of having a 25kg sack of Lamlac in the house is that I never run out of milk for coffee. Two spoonfuls of the creamy-coloured powder is just right. As it says on the label, 'mixes instantly in cold or warm water'. Lambs drink approximately 1 litre each per day during the first seven days and 1.5–2 litres each per day up to weaning. Action Ram insisted on chugging down 1.5 litres by day two. (He was a monster from the outset.)

Lamlac was first manufactured some forty years ago. Its vanilla aroma is addictive, and is a memory starter more potent than Proust's madeleines. One whiff and I am in a state of lambing.

When my daughter was young, all her friends wanted a pet lamb in the sitting room too. Their parents were never so inclined.

~

Young lambs will imprint on humans, and on landscape. A mountain sheep will graze within half a mile of its birthplace. It is the reason mountain farms, and other farms with primitive landscape, are sold with their stock.

Other than bottle-feeding, the other option for the shepherd with the orphan lamb is to immediately foster it on another mother. From about twelve hours after birth, however, a strange lamb is actively rejected. The knack in adoption is to disguise the lamb's smell so that the ewe believes it to be hers.

There are a few ways fostering can take place. Wet adoption is where the birthing fluid from a newborn lamb is transferred to the adoptive lamb so the ewe thinks it is her own. Or there is the age-old method of 'dry adoption', which is to skin the dead lamb, to make a little jacket of the skin to fit the foster lamb. It needs a sharp knife and a strong stomach. To make the jacket, cut up the dead lamb's belly from its anus to within an inch of the throat, cut around base of neck, and around top of legs. Pull the skin off the dead lamb and place over back of live lamb, and wiggle the legs into the four leg holes. It is akin to dressing a baby in a romper suit. Then, for good measure, rub the dead lamb's carcase over the exposed head of the foster lamb to disguise the smell.

I can do it, but I don't. My alternative technique, taught me by Lindsay Lloyd, is to confuse the ewe by spraying her, her own lamb and the foster lamb with scent. So the other essential in my lambing kit is Yves St Laurent's Pour Homme eau de toilette.

True, it does give the cab of the Land Rover an unusually fragrant air. My late father, who was Navy, said of the cab, 'Smells like a cosmetics counter.'

~

As William Youatt notes:

> The most usual false presentations are – the side of the lamb
> pressing against the mouth of the womb, which may be readily
> detected by feeling the ribs – or the back, and then the bones of

the spine can scarcely be mistaken – or the breech, when the bones of the haunch will be immediately recognised. The hand, when oiled or greased, should be introduced into the vagina, and, the foetus being pushed a little back, one of the legs will probably be felt, and may easily be drawn into the passage. Being held there with the left hand, the corresponding leg must be got at likewise, and brought into the passage; after which the delivery will usually be effected without any great degree of trouble. The most dangerous presentations, and the most diffi-cult to manage, are the crown of the head and the breech. In both cases the lamb must be pushed back into the womb. The head must then be raised with the fingers, and brought into the passage in the former case, and in the latter the lamb must be pushed far enough into the womb, to enable the shepherd to bring down the hind-legs, a work not always easily accom-plished, or to be accomplished at all, on account of the manner in which they are extended under the belly.

Pushing either the 'crown' or the hooves (soft now, until they harden) back into the ewe is going against nature. The ewe will be straining to push out, so you have to wait and push between contractions.

Eventually, you literally get a feel for mis-presentations. There are desperate situations, when the head of the lamb is sticking out of the vulva, the lamb's tongue sticking out of its mouth, and the ewe dwindling. Once, in order to save child and mother, I just pulled the lamb out by its head. The ewe made a noise like sea booming inside a cave. But Tiddlywink lived. So did her lamb, Tiddlywink III.

It is quite possible to perform a Caesarian operation on a ewe.

When our black Shetland ewe Chocolate came down prone with twin lamb disease – meaning the ewe was not intaking sufficient nutrition to sustain herself and her charges – we whisked her off in the back of the Land Rover to the vet at Ewyas Harold, who got the lambs out, and the ewe on her feet, in about twenty minutes on the operating table. The operating theatre was a converted garage behind the suburban-style 1930s detached villa.

The lambs were one male, one female. 'No problem naming the girl,' said Jinman. True enough, it was May, so she became May. The boy's name we left to my son, who decided that the boy would be called Action Lamb, an ovine take on his favourite toy, Action Man. Later, when he'd grown into Action Ram, he once tried to kill me, and his amorous escapades were the stuff of local legend.

Genetics I propose, since his mother, Chocolate, was among the wildest sheep I have ever encountered, outside Soays. Putting her in the back of the Land Rover was the only time I had touched her since shearing. She attracted adventure wherever she went. Fortunately, she was as tough as old boots made from sheep leather. After her Caesarian, I brought her and the lambs back to the house and put them in the adjoining small apple orchard. 'It's important she's got the lambs with her,' said Jinman. 'It'll give her the will to live.' One hour after being ensconced in the orchard, she jumped the wire stock fence and hooved up the fields to rejoin the flock on the other side of the lane, at the top of the hill.

Left behind, to the children's delight, were two orphan lambs, needing to be bottle-fed.

The years have taught me that, no matter how much children like bottle-feeding lambs during the day, they prove impossible to rouse for a night shift. Thankfully, lambs are easier to train. One buys a giant bucket with teats, fills it with Lamlac. After a couple of hours' instruction at a week or so of age, the lambs self-serve.

~

Ewes recognize their lambs by a variety of cues. After smell, there is voice, hence the constant *baa*-ing contact calls which fill the days and nights of the country after lambing. The strength of the ewe–lamb bond is determined partly by milk yield, and partly by the ewe's behaviour.

~

How to tell it is spring. In the bottom field, the birds are performing evensong in the copse. The star performer tonight is the recently arrived blackcap. (I can hear why, in its polyphonic song, it is sometimes called the Nightingale of the North.) And all down the valley is the call-and-response of sheep, ewe to lamb and return.

~

It can all go wrong. Inexplicably. One April morning Bledwynn birthed two ewe lambs, perfect in shape and size, and perfectly spotted black on white, like Dalmatians. I checked that they latched on to the teats. I checked she had colostrum. All running thick and creamy.

This was on top of a hill overlooking Dore Abbey. The sun was shining. Spring was in the air, and a spring in my step as I left her to drive to Hereford to pick up something or another. I got tangled up in traffic. A child was thirsty.

I did not get to the top of the hill till four hours later. The lambs were facing each on their sides, like a large mottled butterfly.

Bledwynn was standing over them, possessive. She stamped her feet as I neared.

The lambs were dead. Warm dead. The eyes only just glazing over, and the crows had not yet come to pick them out.

What did I do wrong? Twenty years later, I still do not know why. The silence of the lambs.

~

Around 6 a.m., 28 March. Half a button moon pinned to the sky. Frost. Rising tide of dawn chorus, mostly the thrush family, from the thicket and copse down by the brook. I can hear it – just – above all the bleating and the baaing. Then up from the road field a skylark flies, a trembling, pulsating corpus of song. Ascending in a spiral, the skylark sings, louder and louder, to make his voice heard over the sheep. Notes from his sweet song land around me.

Sheep and skylarks. My shepherd's life.

A sack of ewe-and-lamb feed over my shoulder. Around me, a wool sea of seventy mature sheep, fringed by lambs. Almost impossible to keep afoot. Robin Hood jumps up, belching in my face. Spill some of the sack as a diversion. The sheep ruck and maul over it. I run to the five troughs and start pouring, as quick as can be done. (Keeps you fit, shepherding.) The sheep catch up with me. Body check from Action Ram. One of the Jacobs catches me in the back of the knees with the sharp end of a horn. (By the end of spring, my legs are ringed blue with bruises, as though a drunk or malevolent tattooist had been let loose on them.)

Tip some of the feed in a line on the ground, which is pure

with white ice; as clean and hard as the galvanized metal troughs. (In sheep farming there are never enough troughs, or hurdles.) A steam-cloud of ovine breath.

The concentrate is dietary supplement. But also dispensing it in such a fashion is the quickest, easiest way to check the sheep. They line up either side of the troughs, heads down, wholly occupied. I walk up and down behind them, inspecting the parade with the keen attention of a colonel inspecting his soldiers.

The lambs, with the adults so diverted, stand around looking peeved. Like human children, lambs have a sense of entitlement.

~

Least favourite job in lambing? Castrating the ram lambs. As a child I saw it done with a knife, quick slice of the blade. My grandfather, born in 1904, could remember in turn that as a boy he witnessed castration done with the shepherd's teeth, in the manner described by Youatt in the 1820s:

The lamb being well secured, the operator grasps the scrotum or bag, and forces the testicles down to the bottom of it. He then cuts a slit across the bottom of the bag in a direction from behind forward, through the substance of the bag, and large enough to admit of the escape of the testicles. They immediately protrude through the incision, being forced down by the pressure above. The operator then seizes one of them, and draws it so far out of the bag that a position of the cord is seen; and then, if he is one of the old school, he seizes the cord between his teeth and gnaws through it. This is a very filthy practice, and inflicts some unnecessary pain. The testicle being thus separated, the cord retracts into the scrotum, and is no more seen. The other testicle is then brought out and operated upon in a similar manner. Very little bleeding ensues – and the young one may be returned to its mother. An improvement on this operation, and which any one except of the lowest grade would adopt, is to use a blunt knife instead of the teeth.

I use red rubber rings, applied to the testicles with special pliers, in the first week of the lamb's life. Apparently, it is painless. It makes me wince.

~

A June evening, early, warm, lit by low rose-glow sunlight.

I've got the sheep in for shearing, the gathering of the clans as I like to think of it. Ryelands, Shetlands, Hebrideans, the Suffolk X Shetlands, and Lollipop, the last Jacob.

About a hundred sheep altogether, plus lambs, down in the field by the brook. Most of the adults are lying in the shade of the west hedge, chins on legs, or lying head up breathily chewing the cud.

Sheep are ruminants, meaning they regurgitate food as a bolus from the rumen in the abdominal cavity, re-chew and re-swallow. Cud-chewing.

Healthy mature sheep will chew their cud for several hours each day.

Watching sheep, it is impossible to avoid ruminating oneself. Only with the food of thoughts, and ideas.

I've let the hedges grow up over the last five years, from the flailed, three-foot-high apologies we inherited. (Why are English hedges hacked so low? For the hunt to go over.) The sheep love the new style; the high hedges remind them of the ancestral sheltering cliff face.

Sheep might be sheep to some people, but to themselves they are different tribes with different cultures. The adults of the breeds remain largely aloof from each other, and have different bedding habits. The big Ryelands have the summer prime position, at the bottom closest to the quenching brook. (In winter they have the highest position, driest and away from the cold brook.) Above them, are the Shetlands; above them and spread out into the field, as though enjoying the novelty of sunshine, are the Hebrideans.

From the bedding ground, there are sheep tracks across the field, indented in the earth by generations of sheep. Follow my leader, certainly. Also, keeping to tracks avoids undue damage to the sward, which is food.

Clever animals, sheep.

Nearly all the lambs are in the next-door field, the Bank, playing in their evening gangs. Tag. King of the Castle on a fallen, ancient elm trunk, as dead as bone. Sooty's lamb Pierrot is entranced by his own vertical take-offs, as if his hooves were spring-loaded. What we call 'lamby jumping'. There are other moves. Two ram lambs are mounting each other; two *moorit* (red-brown) ewe lambs are vying in whirligig.

The lambs are playing. They are having fun. It cannot be denied, and the hills are alive with their cackly laughter.

One lamb remains aloof. She is the daughter of Valentine the Ryeland, the last lamb of the year, born yesterday. She is too young and shy to join in the big lambs' games. Around the mother sheep is an invisible circle of security. For a lamb to play away from its mother is a mark of growing up; in the first day of its life the ewe and lamb remain within a metre of each other. The distance between ewe and lamb when both are grazing increases over the next ten days, reaching a plateau of about 20 metres.

Robin Hood's son Little John, the heir apparent, comes bumbling along, between Valentine and her lamb. The lamb cries. The mother bunts Little John out of the way, although he is almost twice her size. The lamb goes to her teats. The lamb's tail wags.

Textbook case: accidental separation in the first few days causes great agitation of both lamb and ewe, and reunion is immediately followed by suckling.

On the mountain, the shadows of soft clouds racing. Below them, soft lambs racing. Mirror match.

~

Only the lambs have access to Bank Field. They enter through a miniature gateway in the hedge, made by placing two upright gateposts 12 inches apart. They can squeeze through, the adults cannot. A lamb relies entirely on its mother's milk for the first two to three weeks of life, though it will nibble grass from ten days old. Afterwards, lambs may be creep fed, either with food in a trough, where the mother cannot get at it, or by letting lambs 'creep' through holes in a fence on to fresh young grass, which having had a long rest from sheep is 'clean'. This is Bank Field.

The adults, meanwhile, rest, chew and defecate. There is already a mat of their black-green dung pellets on the bedding ground. On this über-fertile earth the thistles grow with abandon, and brilliant goldfinches will descend in their charms to feed on the seed heads in October.

Sheep working for Nature.

The lambs in their evening gangs suddenly realize they have become separated from their mothers and start up with plaintive calling. All down the valley lambs take up the mayday.

One lamb finds the narrow entrance back to the mother

field, and the rest follow in a running sheep stream, white, black, brown, piebald. It takes minutes for all the lambs to pass through. There are nearly two hundred of them.

~

I like a bit of agricultural kit. The lambs have a quotidian hand-ful of concentrate 'creep' (HiPeak organic wheat and barley pellets) placed inside the lamb creep feeder, a long metal box on wheels with bars making the access spaces too narrow for adult sheep to get their noses into. The bars can be adjusted by turning a handle, which, for some reason, I find strangely satisfying.

Someone has failed to shut the field gate to Bank Field prop-erly. The lamb creep feeder weighs about 100kg. Action Ram has turned it over, to spill the pellets.

~

In intensive sheep-rearing systems, artificial weaning occurs at ten weeks of age. (These lambs, however, will recognize and will return to the mother after two months' separation, if allowed.) Sheep wean their young naturally from six months of age, usually when the mother again comes into heat. The shep-herd will aid the process by putting the ewe on poorer grazing to 'dry her off'. Ewe lambs continue to follow the dam. Ram lambs do not.

Valentine's lamb still has six months of maternal care – and fun – ahead of her. She is called Valentina. As I say, inspiration for names can be hard to find.

# HOW SHEEP LIVE:
# THE BODY AND MIND OF SHEEP

Summary of Findings on Sheep Cognition. Sheep show compe-
tence in many cognitive domains including memory and
discrimination capacity. They excel especially in executive function and face perception, performing on par with some primates.
These are both high-level abilities based on a number of different neocortical functions, the prefrontal cortex for executive
function and the temporal cortex for face perception within and
across species.

Lori Marino and Debra Merskin, 'Intelligence, complexity, and
individuality in sheep', *Animal Sentience*, 25(1), 2019

What sheep do is determined by what sheep are. Sheep are
artiodactyls and members of the goat–antelope subfamily
within the ruminant family *Bovidae*. They are evolved grazing
herbivores who prefer grass, short roughage and 'browse'
(shrubs). There are seven species of sheep; the best known is the
domestic sheep, *Ovis aries*, and of this domestic species there are
well over 1,200 identifiable breeds the world over.

In this summation, a distinction of sheep is easily overlooked,
something that sets *Ovis aries* apart from other main farmyard

animals such as the cow, the pig and the chicken. Sheep are not woodland animals; they are animals of wide-open spaces, of hill, desert, mountain. Even the most 'developed' sheep will, as a preference, lie on bare dry earth under the hedge as opposed to dry grass, and run uphill from danger, relying on speed from spindly legs, the ability to clamber and a good view, due to the panorama from the attained peak and superlative vision. (Thus the canny shepherd has the handling pens at the top of the field.) Sheep have horizontal, slit-shaped pupils that allow a peripheral field of view of 270–320 degrees, meaning they can see behind themselves without turning their heads; they have binocular vision of 25–50 degrees. They are thought to be able to see in colour and to distinguish between black, red, brown, green, yellow and white. Sheep eyes possess very low hyperopia with little astigmatism; such optics produce a clear-focused retinal image of objects in the middle and long distance. Sight is a vital part of communication and when sheep are grazing they maintain visual contact with each other; each sheep throws its head up to check the position of the other sheep.

Sheep are prey animals. Since sheep like to both spread the flock out and have a panorama, their grazing and efficiency is affected by paddock shape. Ewes grazing in rectangular paddocks graze for less time, have lower intake levels and use forage less efficiently than ewes in square paddocks.

Added to their excellent vision, sheep have an excellent sense of smell. Males (rams) use their vomeronasal organ in the nasal cavity to sense the pheromones of females (ewes) and detect when they are in oestrus, or as we say up on Johnny's farm, 'in season'. The female uses her vomeronasal organ for early recognition of her neonate lamb. The hearing of the sheep is so-so, meaning the wise farmer who requires their attention, after shouting 'Sheep! Sheep!' (and doing so with a sense of sheep-ishness; it is not the coolest thing to call on a hillside), waves the food bucket around. I have never known a sheep refuse to eat pellets of sugar beet – sheep have a sweet tooth – and the liquor-ice smell travels far.

Sheep's feet are made for walking, but also for marking. Sheep, like all other cloven-hoofed herbivores, have two hooves on each foot upon which they walk tippy-toe. Between the hooves is a gland that exudes scent which is transmitted on to the ground as the sheep walks; each member of the flock recognizes the scent given off by other members of the same flock. This is one of the secrets of 'hefting', whereby a flock of sheep never strays outside its own, home territory. The sheep know their land by the smell of it.

On an abrasive surface, such as the hard hills that are the habitat of mouflon, the hooves wear down; on the soft sward of an English green and pleasant paddock, the hooves grow, and keep on growing. Like fingernails. Accordingly, the shepherd has to trim with foot shears. A noisome pedicure.

Sheep also have scent glands in front of their eyes.

How to tell a goat from a sheep? Goats are even stinkier than a ram in 'the season'. A billy goat has a beard and a caudal scent gland that makes him disagreeably smelly to humans; a billy's smell is intensified by his habit of bending his head between his forelegs to catch his urinary spray at the beginning of rutting for two months of the year, November and December usually. Also, horns in the goat rise vertically from the top of the head, as opposed to the V spiral formation in sheep.

Taste is an important sense in sheep in the establishment of forage preferences, with sweet and sour plants preferred and bitter plants more commonly rejected. Touch and sight are also important in relation to specific plant characteristics, such as succulence. Sheep use their ability to discriminate tastes to self-medicate ('zoopharmacognosy') when they are ill. A number of studies show how sheep learn to discriminate between different edible plants using mental categorization, in much the same way chimpanzees have been shown to classify flowers.

Until the early twentieth century, it was common on hill farms for there to be a 'hospital field' where ill stock would be sent for a self-cure. If humans need 'five a day' of vegetables and fruit, how many varieties do full-scale herbivores require on a quotidian basis? More than allowed by conventional lowland agriculture with its silage system, whereby grass is composed of one or two species of plant. I know farmers who will not let their stock go near a hedge, in case it poisons them. Unlikely, but if a sheep is so stupid as to suicide on bryony, it is doubtless because they have lost the ability to judge the good from the bad by our selective breed 'improvement'. One wonders, from time to time, who is stupid, the sheep or us.

Here are some of the unlikely things I feed sheep: ivy, holly (without berries) and 'tree hay', dried summer leaves of lime, ash, willow and hazel. All used to be common fodder for sheep. Here are some of the unlikely things sheep will help themselves to: brambles, ground elder, thistles, roses (to my wife's dismay) and tree bark. In the paddock by the Dulas, where Robin Hood is buried, there was a fine stand of hazels – before, one fine evening, I turned out our flock of Shetlands. Next morning the lovely, lush grass was intact. Every hazel, however, had been stripped white, to the bone. To a height of about five feet. A sheep's back legs, as well as for walking and marking territory, are made for standing on to reach 'browse'. That was my hard first lesson with primitive sheep. (Our Ryelands had never even so much as sniffed at the *Corylus avellana*.) My second hard lesson was that young apple trees are cat-nip to sheep. If proximate, the trees take over sheep's dreams and desires. I have fought border wars with our Hebrideans to keep them out of orchards, including erecting double-height fencing.

Sheep have the oral equipment for variety. They have no teeth in the upper jaw, but the bars or ridges of hard dental pad. A cleft upper lip permits very close grazing: as the animal grazes, it seizes herbage between the dental pad and lower incisors, then jerks its head slightly forward and up to break stems, leaves and grass blades. Thus the herbage is partly bitten and partly torn apart. On grass, the sheep bites close, which by cutting off the short suckers and sproutings causes the grass to grow more. Nothing will more effectively make a thick pasture than its being occasionally eaten down by sheep. Or geese.

A sheep's tongue is raspy leather, and a match for thistles.

It is this eat-everything ability of primitive sheep that makes them the environmentalist's friend, not foe. We use our Shetlands, Ryelands and Hebrideans to clear scrub and restore grassland organically. Our sheep have cleared an orchard of ground elder (after the apple and pear trees were protected by wire-netting wraps), and woodland of a bramble monoculture. Not a drop of herbicide necessary. On grass, primitive breeds promote plant diversity, since they will not unduly favour one species over another, and keep rampant, hegemonic ryegrass in check. Due to their typically hardy and thrifty nature, our rare and native breeds are the best animals for this job. They made the land; the land made them. Indivisible. Symbiotic.

Conservation grazing benefits not only livestock and habitats but also human health through the benefits of consuming meat from animals reared on varied pasture diets. Anyway, meat from conservation grazing tastes better. How could it not? It is pre-flavoured with herbs and flowers before even reaching the cook's kitchen island.

How to tell the age of sheep? There are eight teeth in the lamb's lower jaw at birth, which are sharp and can play havoc with a ewe's teats. Or one's own fingers, if checking their suck reflex. (There are lambs that display the suction power of hoovers.) These are replaced by large permanent teeth, from the centre first, in the following way: one year old – two teeth (centre); two years old – four teeth; three years old – six teeth; four years old – full mouth of eight teeth. After this the teeth get gappy, then fall out, or get broken and worn down to the gums, and the sheep become 'gummers'.

Much of sheep culture is arcane. The age of sheep is not reckoned from the time they are dropped, or by their orthodontics, but from the first shearing. Much of sheep culture is expressed in the lexicon of locality. Generally, however, in this United Kingdom a mature male is called a ram or tup; while still with its mother it was a ram lamb. A mature female is a ewe; while with the mother a ewe lamb. From the time of weaning, which as a rule is about six months, to first shearing at eighteen months, sheep are hoggets. At first shearing, sheep become shearlings. Afterwards, a two-shear ram, a two-shear ewe etc. A wether is a castrated male. That said, in the south of England a weaned ewe lamb before its first shearing is a chilver, and in the north of England and Scotland a weaned ram lamb would be a dinmont. As for orphan lambs raised on the bottle, you could probably place to within fifty miles where you were by the local term. Such as tiddler in Herefordshire, cade in Leicestershire. (See 'bottle-lamb' in the glossary at the back of the book.)

The natural maximum lifespan of sheep is about ten to twelve years; some ewes of some breeds will breeze pass this landmark. There are instances of domestic sheep living to over twenty. (Numerous of ours have reached fourteen, with Sooty taking the farm prize at fifteen going on sixteen.) According to the *Guinness Book of Records*, the prize for ovine longevity goes to a crossbred blackface ewe, nicknamed Methuselina, who was twenty-five years and eleven months old when she fell over a cliff on the Isle of Lewis in 2012. To confound the rules of ovine biology, she still had most of her teeth. As did Sooty on her death. Vets insist that all sheep lose teeth according to the formula laid down in vet school, and that the resultant gappiness indicates age. Some sheep, however, smile a full set in their dotage.

Sheep will bite, in play, in foreplay and in defence, though the sheep's main defences – aside from running – are to kick, and, above all, to butt with the horns – in those breeds still so equipped – and in the absence of horns, the forehead.

The hardness of a sheep's head has to be experienced to be believed. In the long hot summer of 2003 we had some of our sheep on 'tack', rented ground, above the west Herefordshire village of Ewyas Harold. It was a lovely spot, a view clear to Garway Hill, but the old barbed-wire fencing was dilapidated, meaning that Action Ram had escaped like water through a sieve. So I was busy knocking some half-round stakes into the ground at the very corner of the field. The sun was beating down; it was about three o'clock, in August. Suddenly, I was up in the air, then on the ground.

Action Ram, generally a tame, peaceable chap, had butted me with force from behind. I scrambled to my feet, as he backed off, lowered his head, ran forward and banged me full force in my thighs. (Bizarrely, at this moment the derivation of 'ram' popped into my head, a bulb switched on.)

Over I went again. Up I got, again. A human wobble-man. I retreated to the very corner, almost inside the hedge. He stood there, waiting. I started to cautiously move sideways. He ran and butted me. Every time I moved, he backed off, thundered in from about fifteen feet and butted me. After ten minutes, I was only kept upright by the fence. I was on the ropes.

In the end, it was him or me. So as he charged for the tenth time, I stepped aside and swung the axe at his forehead, and hit him – with the flat of the axe blade – full whack. He staggered and backed off. And lived for ten years.

Why did he attack me? To this day, I know not. Generally, he was amiable, hand-reared. Maybe the sun. There was no shade on that high flat field. The ewes had been standing about in groups, shading heads under their flanks.

Perhaps Action Ram was experiencing an overjolt of testosterone. (He was rivalrous with me around the ewes from time to time.) Maybe he thought it was funny. Maybe it was just a bad fleece day for him.

If the exterior of a sheep's head is concrete-like, the interior is subtle and surprisingly cerebral. There is intelligence behind the slit-eyes and the hard head.

~

Sheep are capable of learning. Like dogs, sheep can learn their own name. Action Ram knew his. Despite all the trouble he caused over his ten-year career of rutting and butting, I forgave him everything for one moment of shepherding glory.

He had climbed a stock fence and wandered off over the Dulas brook, and could not be found. Then I got a phone call. 'Your ram's in with our pedigree Lleyn ewes ...' The Land

Rover had broken down, again; the lane to Mrs Price's farm was nearly vertical, and about eight feet wide and windy, so taking the tractor and trailer did not appeal. In the end, I took the family estate car, bright red and German.

'He's over there,' said Mrs Price when I arrived on the yard of her ancient stone farm. 'I can't do a thing with him. Nor the dog.' I called over the stone wall, 'Action!' He looked up. I held up a bucket of sheep nuts. He ran over. I walked around the back of the house, opened the wooden pedestrian gate. Action walked through, followed me on the heel, to the yard. I opened the boot of the car. Put in the bucket, said 'Up!'

Bless him. In he clambered. Off I drove. In the rear-view mirror Mrs Price a standing statue, open-mouthed.

The evidence for judgement in sheep is strong. In tests, when an expected reward for completing a task is less than expected, sheep respond emotionally (with increased cardiac responses and locomotion). Sheep form expectations and have feelings about whether those expectations are met, and can follow a fairly complex set of events leading to an outcome.

Action Ram comprehended what he was doing.

Academic researchers have discovered sheep can navigate complex mazes, and get quicker at doing so the more they practise. Every shepherd will confirm that sheep are rather good at puzzles, if the puzzle is 'How to get past the human-manufactured barrier to the greener grass on the other side?' For a week I was outwitted by our Jacobs who, when placed on one side of a three-string electric fence in the morning, would, by the afternoon, be on the other side, until I caught them in the act. They reversed through the fencing; the wool of their rumps was sufficiently dense to insulate against the shock. Our Hebrideans discovered that, with a fine sense of balance, they were able to walk over a hoof-proof grid at the top of the track to the house.

The ultimate accolade for animal intelligence is to be classified as a tool-user, along with chimpanzees, gorillas and Californian sea otters. According to S.F. Bates in a letter to *New Scientist*, 15 March 1979, sheep can use tools. He reported that Gritstone sheep in Lyme Park, Cheshire, had scratched away snow to reveal hidden grass using pieces of wood they held in their incisor teeth. It seems they used the technique where the snow had thawed and refrozen, becoming hard and icy.

My Hebrideans were able to walk over the cattle grid time and time again, because they have the capacity for memory. Once learned, things are rarely forgotten by sheep. A sheep's ability to recall faces is especially prodigious: a 2001 academic study found that sheep can recognize and remember at least fifty individual faces for more than two years. That is longer than some humans. Like humans and monkeys, sheep 'demonstrate neural, perceptual, and social specialization for faces'.* Or, in lesser academese, sheep can discriminate between individual sheep, between breeds, between sexes, between emotions, between humans. (In the oddest academic experiment ever – a competitive category, you feel – sheep were taught to distinguish photos of celebrities. Even with corrupted photographs, 65 per cent of sheep recognized Fiona Bruce.) Sheep prefer, unsurprisingly, sheep with a calm expression to sheep with a startled expression. On humans they prefer a smile to a frown.

Sheep are quick learners. As food is crucial for sheep survival – domesticated sheep spend up to twelve hours a day grazing – they need to evaluate an entire smorgasbord of

---

\* Kendrick et al., *Nature* 414 (see bibliography).

plantstuff. Is it good, is it bad? The Babraham Institute at Cambridge, by recording the electrical output from single cells in the sheep's brain, discovered that they are single-trial learners. One taste, one lesson learnt. The ability of Larry the Lamb to categorize, rank and recall plants is up there with the chimps'.

Sheep possess emotional intelligence, as well as 'intelligence' intelligence. Watch their ears. In positive mood – such as being fed high-quality organic sheep cake out of a sack – the ears are passive, floppy. Old Robin Hood, when being stroked on his neck by me, would let his ears droop utterly. In negative situations, such as being penned for shearing, the ears are erect, straining forward, like hairy satellite dishes homing in on a target. Under intensive factory-farming conditions, ewes and their lambs are separated at as early as one month and typically between two and four months. This practice causes emotional, and very vocal, distress for the lamb and the mother. Sheep are able to empathize. Ewes pay more attention to their lambs when the lambs are in pain (such as after their tails are 'docked' to prevent infection).

A 2009 report published in *Animal Welfare* found that sheep are capable of experiencing a whole range of feelings, despair, boredom and happiness. Play makes sheep happy. Or, perhaps, happiness makes sheep play.

Sheep know fear too. And fear is an emotional contagion.

~

Tonight both the dog and the vixen fox from Three Acre Wood come up to the lambing paddock. (They have cubs; I've seen them, rough-and-tumbling in the family scrapyard of bone and feathers in front of the den.) The foxes circle the paddock, much as the Apache circled the white man's fort. For hours the beam of the torch catches the flash of two pairs of patrolling emerald eyes. Since the foxes show no sign of desisting, I kick out a Labrador and two terriers from the warmth of the sitting-room fire, because it is time for them to earn their bowl of Wagg Complete Worker (VAT-free).

The dogs do their guard duty, the flock is saved.

Until the next afternoon.

I have a sneaking regard for the sneak-thief that is *Vulpes vulpes*. The soundtrack of spring in hill country is the call-and-response of sheep, ewe to lamb and return. It is constant and rhythmic, in the way that waves gently lapping a harbour wall are constant and rhythmic. But just after 2 p.m., in broad day-light, there is a giant tidal wave of wailing in the paddock. I get there in time to see the vixen in a Mexican standoff with a ewe, whose two lambs are nervous behind her.

Hebridean ewes are horned, and will fight. The fox looks at the ewe, looks at me, and trots off to attack another day. She is drab and fatigued by mothering.

A part of me pities her until I see the lamb at the edge of the ditch, calling down. The vixen has panicked the flock, and a ewe has gone into the ditch, to lie broken and puppet-sprawled at the bottom. Ditch is a misnomer here, for really it is a gorge in the red sandstone, eight feet deep, which takes the run-off from high fields and the farm pond.

The ewe needs killing, humanely. And better to do it quickly myself rather than wait for a vet. So ten minutes later I am slid-ing down the side of the ditch with a 12-bore shotgun and cartridges of BB pellets.

It is a descent into katabasis. The base of the ditch is a shadow world of ferns, moss, slime, serpent ivy, the spine from some unrecognized animal. The coursing water booms echoey off the walls.

I had distracted the flock before the dispatch with a bucket of sheep nuts. But a curious sheep is on the ledge, peering at me. By the time I climb out, the sheep has gone off to the far end of the paddock and told the flock, who stand motionless, staring at me, food forgotten. Ears pointed forward. Every sixty-one of them.

~

Emotion is the driver in the complex acts of loyalty in a sheep's life. Loyalties of kith and kin.

The primary loyalty is mother–offspring. Ewes and their lambs form strong emotional bonds rapidly following birth, provided they are in a suckling relationship. Mothers communicate with their lambs using low-pitched bleats similar to mother–child vocalizations in many other species. As young as twelve hours old, sheep can identify their mothers through sight and sound. Given the chance, mothers and their offspring tend to associate with each other, even after weaning. That afternoon of the fox was the first time I clearly observed this. Sooty was beside her daughter, Soo; Soo was beside her daughter, Soozy. In the tableau, imprinted in my memory, the three are in a row, separate and distinct. Then I see that the flock is composed of similar mini-units.

A flock cannot be understood in haste, or in prejudice. You need time and the wish to know, really know sheep. To see them as they really are.

Such sub-groups may be forged of bonds other than family. Young lambs form strong social bonds with each other. On watching rams for three years, researchers from the University of California discovered that they established supportive friendship: 'Rams were found to form long term relationships ...

[they] intervened on behalf of weaker colleagues and supported each other in fights.'

The bonds can be with other animals (including goats, dogs, cattle). Sometimes a strong bond forms between two madly different animal types and they become mutually dependent. Mary did indeed have a little lamb. Johnny had a large ram called Robin Hood.

Sheep have erotic preferences. About 8 per cent are gay. (Which is tricky when you are trying to breed from them.)

A flock of sheep is not just a flock of sheep. Aside from sub-groups based on family, friendship, sexual orientation, flocks may have hierarchical structures.

A sheep flock is a society. Hierarchies develop among rams, less so among ewes, and top ram invariably has the horns to match. The ram with the horns is the ram with the crown. Our four-horned Jacob ram, Rameses, strutted about the place like the monarch of the glen, and would walk with impeccable imperial swagger to the top of the hill to cast his eyes over his territory and his flock. His dominance was such that he was unable to abide an up-and-coming Hebridean ram in a field fifty yards away. One day I found Rameses dead in front of the metal field gate separating them. He had charged the gate – the front bars of which were stoved in – in an attempt to see off the contender, and had broken his neck. Female sheep, unless protecting themselves or their lambs, tend not to butt, more to push and shove in the competition for food in the trough.

Sheep also have individual personality. Some ewes really are good mothers, others bad ones. Tests of shyness and boldness – based on risk-taking, reactions to novelty, willingness to explore – prove there are sheep who lead, and sheep who follow, regardless of sex or appearance. When we bought our starter flock of ten Hebrideans from north Herefordshire, I dismissed one ewe, who was slight and scrawny. 'I'd take her, if I was you,' said the vendor, Alison Prior. 'She's the lead sheep.' Fortunately, I followed the advice. Hilda, with her Michael Jackson tip-tilt nose, led the flock with matriarchal majesty for eight years.

The complexity of the flock continues, since different breeds have different strength of structure. Merinos are tight-knit and rarely form sub-groups, and will flock blob-like when threatened or driven by the shepherd and his dog. Dorset Horns, on the other hand, always form sub-groups. The more primitive the sheep, as a rule, the more the sub-groups – which is one reason Soays tend to scatter like stones thrown on ice when threatened.

My one experience with Soays was short and bitter. A flock was being dispersed at Bacton. A family friend, Sarah, said she'd like a few of the Soays to keep her overgrown orchard in trim. 'You know sheep, John, can you help me round them up?'

'Of course,' said Farmer John. I drove up to the Soay establishment in full style, Land Rover pulling double-axle Richardson horse-trailer. In the back of the Land Rover, twenty or so hurdles, a roll of stock fencing, ten half-round posts, a sheep trough. In the front of the Land Rover my son, Tris, then aged seven – a good age for running about, impersonating a sheep dog. Sarah arrived, bringing her daughter Kati, also seven, along with her.

The thirty Soays were in a two-acre paddock on the river plain of the Dore, meaning un-usefully flat. Lovely sward, though. Buttercups. Clover. Yarrow. Bird's-foot trefoil, the 'egg and bacon' plant. Meadow fescue. Vernal. Crested dog's tail.

It was hot. Mid May. Just after lunch.

I opened the gate; the Soays exploded to the far end. I walked in, cooing, shaking a bucket.

They were magnificent, like miniature gazelles. In the sun I set up two pens, a large outer one and a small inner one, in the nearest corner. Undismayed by the flatness, I rolled out the netting to form a funnel towards the pens, kept upright by some hastily banged-in posts.

This took an hour. Sarah kept me company. The kids played.

In this hour, the Soays remained on high alert. They did not eat or chew cud. They stood and watched. And waited.

The catching set-up complete, I shook the bucket, called, tipped some feed in the trough and got the rest of the human party to walk slowly along the side of the field towards the sheep, to get behind them . . .

The Soays displayed magnificent contempt for the food. Nor would they be driven towards the pens. Contrary to the standard rules of sheep-keeping, they did not run away. They ran back between us. Through legs. They ran around and around in dizzying gangs of three and four. One ewe went promisingly near the funnel – then jumped the netting clear, in a single bound.

Her lamb tried to go through the netting and I grabbed it. Did the mother come to the rescue, so I could grab her? No. So the lamb was let go.

After half an hour, the sheep were stressed, although not as stressed as me. 'Hopeless,' I said to Sarah, waving my shepherd's crook vaguely in the direction of the Soays. 'I'll lend you some of our Jacobs instead.'

I did so. A week later, I bumped into her. 'How are the sheep?' I asked.

'Fine,' she said, 'although Lollipop keeps knocking the back door to come in for food.'

Lollipop, a four-horned Jacob, was a singular sheep, and

another proof of ovine variety. She was always a loner, self-contained, on the edge of things. She much preferred human company to 'conspecifics', her own kind.

Or she may have simply believed she was human. Or that humans are sheep.

~

That afternoon of the Soays informed my understanding of Greek mythology.

Thalia, the muse of comedy, is usually depicted holding a shepherd's crook. Of course she is.

~

The stereotype: sheep are docile, passive, timid and stupid. Whereas their true behaviour, cognition and personality reveals them as complex, individualistic and social.

Even the most commercially minded sheep farmer might wish to know that ewes placed near familiar companions graze longer than ewes surrounded by unfamiliar conspecifics. That is, that sheep, when happy, feed more.

Happy sheep are healthy sheep. The practical farmer keeps the flock together, including the rams.

Which is the natural order of ovine things.

*John with Tris and Freda, plus Valentine and her lambs.*

## III

# FLEECE AND FLESH

If wool growing is your business, beware of barbed vegetation, goose grass and star-thistle; avoid too rich grazing: choose from the start, a flock both white and soft fleece. Reject any ram, however pure and white his wool, if the tongue beneath his moist palate is black, for he'll breed lambs with blackspotted fleeces – Reject, and look around for another ram on the crowded sheep run. With the lure of such snowy wool, Pan, god of Arcady, tricked the Moon . . .

Virgil, *Georgics*, *c.* 29BC

At the edge of the field, by the brambly hedge, on 2 February, Candlemas: the traditional day on the farming calendar to move livestock off the hay meadow. Over winter, the sheep have eaten off all accumulated roughage, cleaning it up for the new growth of grass.

The mist is thick, and seems to be slowing the Hebrideans as they amble up the field following the old sheep pathways. The sheep step behind each other. To a degree this is follow-my-leader (Hilda), but to a degree it saves effort and health. To the human mind, the trackways wander incomprehensibly; to the sheep, who are the experts in these matters, they are the quickest, driest, easiest route from bedding area to river, from river to the east grazing, from east grazing to the sorrel patch etc. This morning, the north path is the way into Marsh Field.

More than brume slows the sheep. They are heavy and round with lamb. They exude self-satisfied fecundity, which the wet on their coats does nothing to dampen.

There is none of the usual excitement at moving on to fresh grass. Usually when entering a fresh field, the Hebrideans immediately start casing the joint, but to break out rather than in. Fifty convicts wanting escape.

This morning the pace is wholly glacial. The mist depresses us all.

I watch the flock go past, count them, check them, rub my hands to keep warm, wish they would hurry. At last they all go through.

I go to close the gate. I see on the brambles beside the rackety oak gatepost some flags of black wool, caught on the barbs. My fingers pluck a piece. Almost absentmindedly, I twist the wool by rubbing it with my fingers. Collect another tuft. Stretch it, spin it.

Long, long ago, some prehistoric person did the same, and began the history of raising sheep for wool, and of wool as a textile. In the faraway past, the wool so gathered would have been of poor quality, akin to that of the wild mouflon: short, coarse, pigmented brown, bristly. Such sheep would not have been shorn; the wool would have been gathered from bushes and the ground where it had self-divested naturally, or plucked off the sheep's body. Pulling the wool off the sheep by hand is known as rooing. (I occasionally roo some of our unrefined sheep, such as the Shetlands.)

Selective breeding for wool began about 6000 BC, and in that crucible of ovine husbandry, Mesopotamia. There breeders gradually bred out the bristles, and bred in whiteness – white fleeces being more dyeable. The earliest woven woollen garments are dated to around 3000 BC in Babylon (otherwise known as the Land of Wool). If anything, felt-making – where wool is matted and condensed – preceded spinning and weaving. The Ancient Sumerians claimed that the secret of felt-making was discovered by Urnamman of Lagash, a traveller and a Sumerian warrior hero who put wool in his shoes for comfort, to discover that sweat and movement had produced felt socks. The National Museum in Copenhagen has preserved caps made of solid felt from the early Bronze Age, about 3500 BC.

Before felting, before weaving, the skin of the sheep, the hide, was tanned and worn as a kind of tunic.

Hides and felt never really caught on in the West, being unmalleable and uncomfortable. The future was the white stuff, wool and woven, and the invention of the spinning wheel around AD 1200; and the later mechanization of weaving, only made wool more popular.

The hair of the sheep is an overlooked little miracle. Each fibre consists of a protective layer of overlapping cuticle cells that lie, like the slates on a roof, towards the tip. As William Youatt noted:

The filaments of white wool, when cleaned from grease, are semi-transparent; their surface in some places is beautifully polished, in others curiously incrusted, and they reflect the rays of light in a very pleasing manner. When viewed by the aid of a powerful achromatic microscope, the central part of the fibre has a singularly glittering appearance.

You can tell the health of sheep by their shine. Or not. Glossiness is healthiness. As with humans.

Each cell of the wool filament has a waxy coating that repels water from the root but allows water vapour to be absorbed. On the sheep's back this means the fleece can absorb up to 30 per cent of its weight in rainwater (or snow) but not lose its insulating properties. When removed from the sheep, the wool can absorb dye without collapsing into mush.

Wool is flexible, and fireproof. Wool is natural. Wool: what's not to like?

~

'The Dumfries House Declaration' of The Campaign for Wool (Patron: HRH The Prince of Wales) points out further that:

*Wool forms part of a natural carbon cycle*:
Sheep consume organic carbon by eating plants, and store this in their fleece. Fifty per cent of a fleece's weight is pure organic carbon stored in a durable, wearable form.

*Wool is a natural alternative to wasteful consumer practices*:
Research shows that the average life of a Wool garment is 2–10 years, compared to 2–3 years for garments made from other fibres.

*Wool was made for recycling*:
Wool fibres are high quality and durable, capable of re-use and recycling, ultimately reducing landfill disposal. Wool is routinely upcycled into woollen-spun knitwear, insulation and geotextiles – all of which contribute to a circular economy.

*Wool is biodegradable*:
Wool decomposes in a matter of years, releasing valuable
nitrogen-based nutrients back into the soil.

*Wool is naturally odour resistant*:
By absorbing moisture vapour, Wool garments leave less
perspiration on the skin, reducing odour-causing
bacteria. Easily refreshed by airing, Wool garments can
be worn longer between washes due to Wool's natural
ability to shed dirt and bacteria.

*Wool improves indoor air quality*:
When used in interior textiles such as carpets and
upholstery, Wool absorbs and locks away pollutants such
as volatile organic carbons (VOCs) from the air more
rapidly than other fibres.

~

Numerous of the early civilizations begat a wool industry:
Babylonians, Sumerians, Persians. Numerous bible figures kept
large flocks. The Romans, however, were the master flock-
keepers.

What did the Romans ever do for us?. They came, saw, con-
quered and founded the English wool trade.

The Romans had bred sheep for wool, as distinct to
flesh, from the third century BC. In his agricultural opus
*De Re Rustica*, written about AD 60, Columella rated the sheep
of Altino (near modern Venice) and Tarentum, in southern
Italy, as the providers of the finest fleeces. The point
being, of course, Columella's recognition of differing quality,
or 'grading'.

After the invasion of Britain in AD 43, the Romans introduced a longwool Apulia-type sheep with a pure white fleece,
a beast twice the size of the Celtic little brown sheep running
around the isles, and with a fleece four times heavier. In England,
the Romans concentrated the wool flock around their principal
centres of population: Lindum (Lincoln), Camulodunum (Col-
chester), Cirencester, Romney Marsh. All these places are still
connected with the English longwools.

At first, the wool from the Roman sheep in England was
mostly exported to their factories in northern Gaul but by
AD 50 they established a manufactory at Winchester, making
garments for the civilian population and the army. English
wool was in demand because it made garments of top quality,
and a Roman's social status was proclaimed on his and her
body. (Scouring – the removal of natural oils and dirt – was
achieved by immersing the bolts of wool in vats of stale human
urine and then having slaves tread them. By the Middle Ages
fuller's earth was preferred, which is a type of clay with the
power to absorb the lanolin and cleanse the wool.)

After the Romans left, the English wool trade did not dis-
appear. English flocks continued to produce high-quality wool
irrespective of who ruled. Wool was money, was power, was a
national endeavour. The Saxon king Edward 'sette his sons to
scole, and his daighter he set to woll werke'. The very name by
which unmarried women in Britain are still designated, spin-
sters, is proof of the antiquity and importance of wool-work.
To fund wars, monarchs, starting with King Edward, slapped
taxes on the export of wool. The Norman conquerors, looking
to maximize revenue from the enslaved land, set up the offi-
cious Wool Staple (from the medieval Latin *stabile emporium*,
meaning fixed mart.) From 1314, this government monopoly

levied duty on the totality of raw wool exported. The Staple lives on in the shape of the British Wool Marketing Board, with its statutory monopoly over the sale of British wool.

Wool became big business in the medieval age. Everyone who had land, from peasants to peers, raised sheep. The major players were inevitably the arriviste Norman aristocracy and their monastic houses, in particular the Cistercians, whose flocks grew to be extravagant size. The Cistercian house at Melrose had twelve thousand sheep.

White wool was aided by Black Death. After the plague of 1347, manpower became so scarce that laborious manorial cultivation became impossible. Large acreages of arable land became pasture, colonized by the grasses and wild flowers that grow naturally in the British climate. From the Cairngorms and Pennines in the north, down through the Cotswolds to the rolling hills of the West Country, across to the southern Downs and manors of East Anglia, Britain went under the hoof.

Wool made the landscape and fortune of Britain. In 1341 Parliament had granted Edward III 30,000 sacks of wool; assuming a fleece of about one and a half pounds in weight and a content of 364lb wool per sack, we can see that this levy alone implies a population of 7,280,000 sheep of shearable age. The nations depended on it: in the last year of Henry V's reign (1421–2), out of a total Crown income of £55,750, £35,000 came from wool. To symbolize the pre-eminence of the wool trade in England's medieval fortune, woolsacks were situated in the House of Lords. To this day the seat of the Lord High Chancellor in the House of Lords is a large square bag of wool.

Most of the medieval wool was exported. Flemish and Italian merchants were ever present in wool markets of towns, ready to buy wool from lord or peasant alike, for ready cash.

The pre-eminence of English wool is reflected in the world-wide acceptance in the wool trade of longstanding English terms and standards. English wool graders devised the 'Bradford' or 'Spinning' Count, a measure of assessing the fineness of wool. It is an estimate (relying on the eye of the grader) of the number of hanks (a hank is 560 yards) of single-strand yarn that can be spun from a pound of 'top', which is washed wool combed to make all the fibres lie parallel. Wool counts range from 36s to 80s.

The Bradford Count was used across the world for centuries, until it was superseded by measurement by microscope expressed in microns (0.001mm). A Bradford Count of 74s would now be 18 microns, whereas a count of 36s would be 38 microns.

## Confessions of a Sheepophile I

I grew up with animals, pets and livestock both. So I knew they were sentient, and that I could be in relationship with them. Communicate with them, even.

Even so, I misjudged our first sheep, Bledwynn and One Puppy. We brought them home, put them in the old apple orchard next to the house. They immediately did what I hoped, which was to put soul into the landscape. (Their clearance of the ground elder was an unexpected bonus.) Farmland without livestock is emotionally barren. It also raises the worrisome eco question of how the land is being fertilized without them.

To our amusement, Bledwynn and One Puppy matched in all they did, like synchronized swimmers, or a crowd watching a tennis match. They grazed at the same time, birthed at the same time, drank at the same time, watched the dogs with apprehension in the same way. The sameness of sheep, I thought.

Then the subtleties of personality and sisterhood began to be noticed. One Puppy, coquettish and mischievous (and notably glamorous in her markings, black beauty spots all over), was very much the younger sister; Bledwynn, rangier and plainer (a couple of indistinct black splodges on the coat), was entirely more sensible. She also groomed her sister more, making sure she was properly turned out.

We had them for eight years. And then one morning I went into the field, and there lying in the centre among the ant hills was One Puppy. I thought she was sleeping. She was dead. Standing over her was Bledwynn, who, when I tried to retrieve One Puppy's body, stamped her front hoofs.

I talked to the vet. No obvious cause for One Puppy's death. 'One of those things.' Possibly age, since she was ten. As a precaution I moved the sheep off the grazing.

The next day, Bledwynn died. You see, the mystery is: no other sheep expired. One Puppy and Bledwynn were sisters, were friends. I wonder to this day if Bledwynn died of a broken heart.

~

Although most commercial production of wool now comes from descendants of Spanish merino sheep (introduced by the Beni-Merines, a tribe of Arabic Moors in the twelfth century AD), the sheep that made Britain's medieval wealth were homegrown, native stock, and of two principal types. The first was a small sheep producing short wool from poor pastures, hills, moors and downs. Of this sort Ryeland was the most famous breed, grown on unimproved grassland pastures between the Severn and the marches of Wales. (Counter-instinctively, sparseness of pasture makes wool fibres finer.) The Leominster Benedictine priory kept large flocks on its granges and eventually 'Lemster Ore' became the term used to describe the precious fleece off the Ryeland's back.

One Italian merchant recorded the prices for English wool between 1317 and 1321. 'Lemster Ore', the golden fleece, was worth 28 marks per sack of 364lb. (A mark was two-thirds of a pound.) At today's prices 28 marks would be worth the equivalent of £3,000. When I've sheared Ryelands I've received about £180 a sack. Then again, the modern Ryeland has been crossed numerous times in unwise ways to improve the carcase, and the rule of 'improvement' is more meat, lower quality wool.

Lemster Ore was one of the finest wools in Europe. Queen Elizabeth I insisted that her hose be made only from Lemster Ore, refusing to wear any other. The sixteenth-century bucolic poet Michael Drayton celebrated its virtues:

*Where lives a man so dull, on Britain's farthest shore*
*To whom did never sound the name of Lemster Ore*
*That with the silkworm's web for smallness doth compare.*

By the 1600s there were at least twelve million sheep in Britain.

~

One Ryeland stands square, and spins its alabaster torso so the wet sprays off in a brief abdominal halo. We have looked at one another a lot, Ryeland sheep and my family, on mornings like this over the years, because Ryelands and I are the dangling ends of dynasties long familiar to each other. My mother's maternal line, the Parrys, had Ryelands grazing here in these meadows under the Black Mountains five hundred years ago. And I like to think it was cousin Blanche Parry who gave Elizabeth I the stockings made from fine, white Ryeland wool which so impressed the Queen she would thereafter have no other material on her virginal legs. Blanche Parry served Elizabeth for fifty-six years as lady-in-waiting.

~

The longwoolled sheep of England's fortunes were the Lincoln and Cotswold breeds. Lincolns carry heavy locks down to the knees (occasionally lower still), with ewes giving fleeces of 5–9kg. Although coarse and hair-like, the fleece has considerable lustre. The Cotswold breed, from the hills above Gloucester, became known as the Cotswold Lion for its leonine, corkscrew curls. It was the golden fleece that paid for the area's famed golden buildings.

By the sixteenth century, England's wool trade was already in its long decline. The causes were straightforward. Merino wool had started to improve in quality, long wars interrupted the export trade, and over-taxation prompted European textile producers, including the Flemish, to switch to Spanish merino wool.

Some attempts to stem the decline in the British wool trade were notable. In the 1570s a law was passed that all Englishmen except nobles had to wear a woollen cap to church on Sundays, part of a government plan to support the wool industry. A swing to manufacture of woollens, rather than exporting the raw material, helped. Leeds became the smoky centre of a cloth-making industrial revolution. Then there was tweed, and tartan.

~

Depending on your perspective, the Highland Clearances of eighteenth-century Scotland were either a bid by rapacious landowners to make a fast guinea, or the means by which the rule of law was brought to regime-change-seeking Catholic rebels (the 'Jacobites'). Whatever the cause, the Highland Clearances razed thousands of turf-walled homesteads to leave vast tracts of Scotland nigh on uninhabited. The empty land was given over to Blackface and Cheviot sheep.

Scotland had the space and the sheep. Scotland also had the engineering wit, and fashion nous. In the eighteenth century, a trio of Scottish inventions transformed the local cottage weaving industry based around a pattern of checks in white and grey or brown called 'the shepherd's plaid'. (The traditional dress of rural Scotsmen for centuries; a similar pattern of cloth was described by Tacitus as the dress of the Celts the Romans encountered in the Borders.) These new devices were the flying shuttle of John Kay (which allowed a broader cloth to be woven), the water-driven power-loom, and the Teasing Willy (which 'carded' or pulled apart the wool to facilitate easier spinning). A building spree of water-powered woollen mills in Borders Scotland ensued – to the dismay of William and Dorothy Wordsworth, who bemoaned that the pretty village of Galashiels had become 'a townish bustle' – and it was these manufactories that made the trade of tartan and tweed.

Tweed was invented by two Scottish clothiers relocated to Victorian London, Archibald Craig and James Locke. The fashion of the time was for jackets and trousers to be made from different patterns of cloth – morning dress is a surviving fragment of this – but when the Prince of Wales appeared in public in a jacket and trousers that 'suited' one another a new sartorial fashion was set, and Borders manufacturers satisfied it by producing lengths of 'tweel' or 'twill' in huge quantities. In 1847 Locke, according to legend, received a consignment of 'tweel' from William Watson's dangerfield mill at Hawick. Due to a blot on the label accompanying the consignment, Locke's clerk misread tweel as 'tweed'. Making the name of the cloth synonymous with Borders river Tweed was a touch of marketing genius. Tweed has never since lost its appeal.

Tartan has a yet more fabulous origin. In 1815, Colin Macrae, the secretary of the London Highland Society (a club of ex-pat Scotsmen), wrote to the clan chiefs asking them to submit a sample swatch of their clan tartan for a registry of such. Most of the clan chiefs had never heard of tartan; luckily there were plenty of manufacturers willing to remember their patterns for them. The enterprising Sobieski-Stewart brothers, John and Charles-Edward, half Polish half Scottish adventurers who claimed a tenuous descent from Bonnie Prince Charlie, compiled a catalogue of all the 'ancient clan tartans' in their wholly invented book, *Vestiarum Scoticum*. This appealed powerfully to Scottish sentimental nationalism, both at home and abroad.

When George IV swathed himself in tartan, including a kilt for a visit to Scotland, he set a trend for subsequent monarchs to follow, and gave tartan priceless advertising. Tourists loved it, as much as the Scots. Romantic Scotland – the Scotland that adorns shortbread tins – had already received a massive prompt from local novelist Sir Walter Scott (1771–1832), the scribe of *Waverley*, *Rob Roy*, *The Bride of Lammermoor* and all. Scotland in Scott's novels was sublime, picturesque, chivalric.

Army regiments in Scotland were also granted access to the

tartan dressing-up box, the whole shebang of plaid kilts, trews and fancy sporrans.

Quite a lot of the tartan military get-up was pure invention. In the words of the Edinburgh historian Trevor Royle, author of *The Flowers of the Forest: Scotland and the First World War*, the tartan 'turkey-cock' look was one of the nation's several 'dubious military traditions'. Regiments with barely a passing familiarity with plaid bedecked themselves in it. But tartan served a purpose: dressing up in tartan and sporrans put clear plaid water between Scottish regiments and English regiments, between the cultures of Edinburgh and of London. The Scots needed something to withstand the tide of anglicization, as well as to make money: tartan did the job.

~

July 3. Here comes the summer. At last.

I'm down by the brook, taking a break from 'topping', meaning towing behind the International tractor a flat mower to kill the docks, the farming adage being 'June is too soon, in July they die'.

I like to think of myself as a farmer with an alter-eco. I do not mind a few docks – indeed I have left a patch, about 10m x 10m, to mature into seed for the wintering wildlife that need it – but I also need some grass for the cattle. Normally, I would have got the sheep to clear unwanted docks by 'mob-stocking' Bank Field but for wet weeks it has been, effectively, under water.

Sheep, with the exception of North Ronaldsay from up in Scotland, are not aquatic. (I know the feeling; unless it's the Med, Nature's water is too cold.) So this year I'm topping.

After two hours on the tractor seat, time for a break, a sit-down and a cheese and tomato baguette (kept in greaseproof paper in the cab-door pocket; I have been known to take lunch while behind the wheel and baguettes have less tendency to fall apart than sandwiches), taken under a bankside oak, where one sole and ancient bough protrudes into the field. A personal parasol. The sun is already in the west.

After 'spating', the brook is barely moving. Indeed, little is moving. There is no breeze. The birds are quiet. Some flies buzz about, desultory.

Edith, my black Labrador, who has been supervising proceedings, comes and lies beside me.

On the far side of the field, the sheep are under the hedge, edged into the narrow band of shade. A long line of a hundred and twenty sheep (Hebrideans, Shetland and the crosses being gathered for shearing) in a single file stretching from field bottom to top, chewing the cud. From time to time one stands, shakes its head, stops still – as though playing musical chairs, and the music has stopped.

This is the sheep's strategy for avoiding pesky, pesty blowflies.

One sheep detaches itself and trots across to me.

Action Ram. He arrives, looks expectant.

Edith raises her head, looks wary. She has been beaten up more than once by a sheep.

At school, I once had a fight with a guy called Guy. Afterwards, we became friends. Since that fight with Action Ram on the high field, we have been absolute buddies. (Which is all very male, of course.) I give his velvet brown nose a stroke – and the crisp end of the baguette.

Since I am sitting, and he is standing, we are eye to eye.

In the eye of a sheep there is what? The slit-band of the iris takes the attention with its focused intentionality. Above and below the iris, all manner of emotions can be discerned. At this moment, Action Ram's eyelids have shuttered minutely.

In pleasure, in relaxation.

If it were cooler, he would probably persist in wheedling more treats by pawing at me.

This July afternoon it is too hot, so instead he flops down, on the other side of me to Edith, his back legs sprawled one way, his head between his front legs. All of us in the shade.

The lion may lie down with the lamb. The Labrador with the ram.

~

During the second half of the twentieth century, the price of wool sank so low it cost more to shear the sheep than its wool was worth. Some farmers buried wool rather than lose money on ferrying it to a British Wool Marketing Board depot (BWMB).

If you have four or more adult sheep in the UK, you are legally required to register with the BWMB and market your fleece wool through it, with the exception of Shetland producers, who negotiated an exemption, and those who apply successfully for derogation. These are largely the keepers of sheep with coloured fleece, for which there is a very limited industrial use. Such fleeces tend to go to hand-knitters and home-felters.

All British fleeces – except the exemptions – arrive at the BWMB's Bradford warehouse or one of its regional depots from the farm in 'sheets' – big sacks about 6 feet square, each packed with about fifty fleeces. The annual clip of wool is sold at one of the fortnightly auctions held at the Wool Board's HQ in Bradford, with the Board paying its members – effectively almost all of Britain's commercial sheep farmers – a price based on the average over the year. All wool is auctioned and producers receive two payments – an advance payment when wool is delivered to the depot and a balance payment the following year, along with that year's advance payment.

The BWMB was set up in 1950 under the British Wool Marketing Scheme and is now a producer co-operative responsible for the marketing of fleece wool in the UK. The organization's main objectives are:

> To market wool at the lowest cost consistent with efficient service.
> To improve the standard of British wool production.

The UK annually produces over 22,000 tonnes of wool from about 23 million sheep.

~

If you are a farmer, you may be totting up the wisdom of sheep-keeping. Meat prices are low, and the days when the 'clip', the shearing of the flock, was a real money-earner, enough to pay the rent, have long gone.

The wool days are over, but one can still make money off the sheep's woolly back. Tris and my wife christened that costly £15 ewe Shortbread, and she made her money back, again and again. A farmer neighbour, as we chatted away at the top of Bacton overlooking the Golden Valley, declared the Shetlands 'gentleman farmer's sheep'.

'No money in those joints,' he said, casting his eyes over the gate.

'Not *that* much,' I agreed. 'The real value is in the fleece.'

He narrowed his eyes. 'How much?'

I pointed to the shorn Shortbread. 'Twenty-five pounds.'

She really did have a good fleece.

This was the late 1990s, and we were selling Shetland fleeces – raw, untreated – for an average of £10 a pop. In the low sheep market of the time, this was more than the sheep cost. The economics of farming are frequently a bonfire of the sanities.

I had even higher commercial hopes for Shortbread's grand-daughter, Shortcake (whose mother was . . . Biscuit). There is a photograph of me holding Shortcake when she was a two-day-old lamb. She is gold-coloured, and the look on my face is smug, and lascivious. The face of the farmer whose sheep has laid a lamb with a golden fleece.

Like life, Shortcake went beige.

~

The classic method of shearing a sheep is exactly described by William Youatt:

> Everything being arranged a shearer seizes a sheep, and sets it on its rump, and keeps it in this position by resting the back against his own legs. He removes all straws, thorns, burs, &c., that may have adhered to the wool. While thus held, the wool is removed from the head and neck so far as the shoulders, and also from the belly, the scrotum, and the edge of the thighs. The head of the animal is then bent down sidewise, and the shearer, placing a leg on each side of the neck of the sheep, pushes out the opposite ribs by pressing his knees gently against the ribs that are nearest to him. He next shears the wool from the far side with his left hand, from the belly to the middle of the back, and as far down as the loins. The sheep is now turned, and the right hand is employed to shear the wool from the near side.

The sheep is then laid flat on its side, and kept down by the shearer with his face toward the rump of the sheep, resting his right knee on the ground in front of the neck, and his right toe being brought to the ground a little behind and below the poll; the head and neck of the sheep are thus confined by his right leg, while he uses his right hand to shear the wool from the hind quarter. In this way the clips of the shears will appear in concentric rings round the body of the sheep. The dirty portions of wool about the tail are then removed by the shears and kept by themselves; the outside of the fleece is folded inward, beginning at the sides, and narrowing the whole fleece into a stripe about two feet wide. This stripe is then rolled firmly up from the tail end toward the neck, the wool of which is stretched out and twisted into a rope, and wound round the fleece to give it a cylindrical shape.

What Youatt omits to mention is that sheep do not enjoy being sheared. They dislike penning – being pulled through a 'race' (walled corridor) on to a wooden shearing board – and they especially dislike being set on their rump. It is unnatural, which is why it succeeds. They are off balance, physically and mentally. They are afeared into immobility.

I talk to the sheep during shearing. Banter and clichés and platitudes. 'How are you, Sooty?' 'How's the family?' 'Mild for this time of year, no?' Much as the human barber chats inanely and inconsequentially to his customers. They seem to like it.

I know one old shepherd who sings his shearing sheep to soporific relaxedness. Unfortunately I cannot sing.

Sheep differ from each other under the shears. As a rough rule, there is a direct relation between wildness and immobility: the wilder the sheep, the more scared, and the more still it will sit. Sheep used to being handled are under-awed by the event. Within that spectrum, personality shows up. Robin Hood was good-natured under the blade, Action Ram put up a fight from the moment he saw the shears (and closed his eyes as I clipped around his balls), and Sooty was gentle and utterly composed, an aristocrat condescending to let the footman remove her warm coat.

De-fleeced, a sheep is almost unrecognizable, a separate species. A large naked blind mole, something of that ilk. On a very close shave, I can see down to the sheep's skin. Over the years the skin of our sheep has reddened. Their skin has become imbued with the colour of Herefordshire clay. The iron in the soil has entered the skin. They have become part of the earth, and the earth has become part of them.

~

There are sheep intrinsically difficult to shear, irrespective of their place on the wild/tame graph, or their individual personality. Their morphology makes them so, such as four-horned Jacobs.

On my animal farm, two horns are good, four horns are bad. Two horns are 'handlebars' by which the sheep can be manoeuvred. With four horns, there are two surplus horns, which stick up near vertically. Trying to lean over these prongs to shear, or foot trim, results in a poked chest.

~

Some years ago, I betrayed my own rule, which is you have to like your livestock. So I bought, to add to the Jacobs, Ryelands and Shetlands, a dozen Hebridean sheep – small, black, horned, primitive. A neighbour donated a ram: 'Rammy'. The

Hebridean is a productive little sheep. But they escape, and jump like deer. Today I have them in for shearing and one leaps the holding pen into where I am wielding the electric shears. She then tries to vault over me, and only by diving to the side do I avoid her head, which is made from tombstone. Shearing is fine in your twenties; in your forties it kills. The definition of 'back-breaking' should be 'a prolonged period of shearing sheep in the New Zealand style'. Almost everyone shears the New Zealand way, which is to put the sheep on its arse, back to one's legs, and shear down with electric clippers in a particularly rhythmic fashion. (The technique was invented by the Bowen boys in the 1940s; the *Guardian* described Godfrey Bowen as having arms that 'flow with the grace of a Nureyev shaping up to an arabesque'.)

I start off at a reasonable(ish) rate of a sheep every two minutes, the clippers neatly sliding under the line of yellow risen lanolin in the fleece; by sheep number 22 I am down to a sheep every five minutes, and starting to make 'double blows', or two strokes of the shears, because the first isn't close enough. I also nick one ewe's skin badly, and have to blast her with purple spray. By sheep number 26 I am 140 years old. By sheep number 31 I cheat. I park the tractor on the track so no one can surprise me, and shear the rest of the flock with the sheep standing up, a halter around their heads, tied to a gate. I sit down to do it. But I can never tell anyone about it because it is so seriously uncool. My back is broken, and the exertion has turned me into the portrait in Dorian Gray's attic. My hands, though, are baby soft from the lanolin in the fleeces.

~

My poor conscience regarding shearing sheep while they are standing was ameliorated on reading Thomas Firbank's *I Bought a Mountain*, his account of sheep farming in North Wales in the 1930s. In Snowdonia, at least, the shearers sat on benches for the de-fleecing. Back then, shearing was a communal enterprise. When Firbank's flock of 1,200 sheep required shearing, forty men sat on the benches, hand-shearing, sorting, carrying, putting on the owner's marking (with pitch), dabbing picric acid on the cuts on the sheep's body. The people helping were fellow farmers, their sons and daughters, villagers in want of a day's work. It was 'a social event of the greatest magnitude'.

Today, it is just me. Across the valley, it is just Geoff. Up the hill, just Rob.

And our sheep.

I still have sixty to shear.

~

With our first two sheep, the Jacobs One Puppy and Bledwynn, I hand-clipped them with manual shears (essentially large scissors). When we reached twenty sheep a year later, my mother – a farmer's daughter – took one look at the flock, the exhausted me, and said, 'I'll buy you electric shears for your birthday.'

More than twenty years on, the Listers are still going strong.

Another photograph: me (looking very young) holding up a fleece, the first whole one I got off a sheep's back. Intact. No faults. Some events of my life are consigned to the oubliette; others have pride of place on the mental trophy shelf. My first fleece is up there with passing my driving test, an A* at A-level History, winning the record for 200 metres at school.

Even a touch of truth does nothing to tarnish the image. The fleece belonged to Cardigan, a moorit Shetland. Shetlands are the easiest of sheep to shear since the fleece semi-lifts of its own accord.

~

When wool was king, the flesh of the sheep was cheap meat. The animal was dispatched only after a useful working life as textile-provider and walking muck-spreader. Anybody with money ate beef, the jolly carnivorous Englishman's dish of choice. So under-valued was mutton that fat from sheep for tallow candles was worth more than the actual carcase.

It was not until the eighteenth century that sheep were kept primarily for meat. This switch over was an ovine case of 'chicken and egg', or at least lamb and fleece. The long decline in the British wool trade caused farmers to eye up their sheep and consider a more profitable usage. Improving the species for meat, however, entailed a drop in the quality of fine English wool, meaning it generated yet less revenue. England's great wool sheep, such as the Lincoln and the Ryeland, became pale ghosts of their lustrous medieval selves.

The canniest of the sheep men of the 1700s was Robert Bakewell of Dishley Grange in Leicestershire, born on the family farm on 23 May 1725. Before Bakewell, stock breeding had infamously been the meeting and mating 'of nobody's son with anybody's daughter'. Bakewell created from the old Leicester Longwool the sheep that became synonymous with his name, the Dishley (or New) Leicester. As William Youatt explains it:

It was about the middle of the last century, that Mr. Bakewell of Dishley in Leicestershire first applied himself to the improvement of the sheep, in that county. Up to this time, very little attention had been given to the breeding of sheep. Two objects alone appear to have engrossed the attention of the breeders: first, to breed animals of the largest possible size; and, secondly, such as should produce the heaviest fleeces. Aptitude to fatten, and symmetry of shape, that is, such shape, as should increase as much as possible the most valuable parts of the animal, and diminish in the same proportion the offal, were entirely disregarded. Mr. Bakewell perceived that smaller animals increased in weight more rapidly than those very large ones; and that they consumed so much less food, that the same quantity of herbage applied to feeding a larger number of small sheep, would produce more meat than when applied to feeding the smaller number of large sheep which alone it would support. He also perceived that sheep carrying a heavy fleece of wool possessed less propensity to fatten, than those which carried one of a more moderate weight. Acting upon these observations, he selected from the different flocks in his neighborhood, without regard to size, the sheep which appeared to him to have the greatest propensity to fatten, and whose shape possessed the peculiarities which he considered would produce the largest proportion of valuable meat, and the smallest quantity of bone and offal. In doing this, it is probable that he was led to prefer the smaller sheep, still more than he had been by the considerations above stated, because it is found, that perfection of shape more frequently accompanies a moderate-sized animal than a very large one. He also was of opinion that the first object to be attended to in breeding sheep, was the value of the carcass, and that the fleece ought always to be a secondary consideration. The reason for this is obvious: the addition of two or three pounds of wool to the weight of a sheep's fleece, is a difference of great amount; but if to procure this increase, a sacrifice is made of the propensity to fatten, the farmer may lose by it ten or twelve pounds of mutton. The sort of sheep, therein, which Mr. Bakewell selected, were those possessed of the most perfect symmetry, with the greatest aptitude to fatten, and rather smaller in size than the sheep then generally bred.

The blood of Dishley's New Leicesters runs through the veins of every major meat-sheep in the West. He took a long-framed, slow-maturing sheep and made it into a short-legged, hornless, barrel-bodied meaty one. He reduced the inedible parts of the carcase – the bone in particular – and in so doing produced more meat from each animal in the quickest time with the least food. Bakewell memorably declared 'all is useless that is not beef', meaning that the farmer's goal should be a sheep carcase with valuable cuts of meat, not bone or wool or fat. The new sheep, surprisingly, bred true to type. (Always a difficulty with selective breeding.) In other words, offspring had the same traits as the parent.

There were justified complaints that Bakewell's innovation ruined the old Longwool's glory, its fleece, and that the New Leicester had a heavy front end and ran to fat too easily. Bakewell responded with the pep and pepper characteristic of the man: 'mutton *anywhere* was welcome to the poorest classes'. It was. Britain was turning into a nation of meat-eaters, setting a trend to become common across the globe following industrialization. Meat demand rises in line with higher incomes and urbanization.

Bakewell was far from being the sole Great Improver. In Sussex, John Ellman (1753–1832) of Glynde created, out of the area's native short-woolled heath breed, the first modern Downland sheep, the Southdown, a meat sheep for the London market. This improved Southdown was much favoured by aristocrats, notably

Thomas Coke of Holkham and the Duke of Bedford at Woburn, and other gentlemen farmers, largely because the mutton was gauged a finer quality than the New Leicester's, which was considered fit only for hoi polloi. The blood of Ellman's Downland, like Bakewell's Leicester, came to colour breeds galore, especially in the New World. The Shropshire Down, a cross between a Southdown and a local Midland or Welsh border sheep, was described in 1911 as 'the most ubiquitous sheep extant', having been exported to every continent. A modern Downland star is the Suffolk, a short-woolled black sheep of Saxon origin, always easy to recognize in the field because it has black Labrador ears. The breed sires a meaty carcase, as Action Ram our inadvertent Suffolk x Shetland ram proved by the hundred.

~

This *is* sheep country.

Over the centuries, sheep breeds in Britain came to suit particular localities or particular purposes. While these native breeds have come and gone, the UK still has fifty-seven autochthonous sheep types (of which twenty-five are considered rare), more than any other country in the world. Add established cross-breeds, and there are ninety types of sheep trotting across the moor and meadow in Britain. This abundance of choice has enabled British farming to establish a 'stratified' or 'pyramid' breeding system that amalgamates the toughness, agility and motherliness of shaggy hill sheep, such as Swaledales, with more prolific-breeding upland strains – Bluefaced Leicester – and then pairs those offspring with an Orwellian-sounding 'terminal sire' (meat-quality-improver ram) from a chunky, fast-maturing lowland breed such as the Suffolk. The result is 'fat lamb' for slaughter.

'Fat' in sheep language does not mean fat – it means mature, and that the animal has reached a stage of growth when the muscle is developed, and there is a layer of fat over the carcase.

In stratification, the British breeds are divided into separate classes:

*The mountain and moorland breeds* – suited to the hardest, highest (and wettest) conditions. Due to poor conditions are often slow-growing, and not very productive. Quality of meat is good, though the carcase of the lamb is not heavy. Wool is usually long and coarse.

Scottish Blackface
Swaledale
Rough Fell
Lonk
Herdwick
Welsh Mountain
Exmoor Horn
Derbyshire Gritstone

*The grass hill breeds* – suited to lower and less hardy conditions than the mountain breeds.

Cheviot
Kerry Hill
Clun Forest
Beulah Speckled Face

*The meat breeds (sometimes called Downs or Shortwools)* – kept mainly to produce rams for crossing with other breeds for meat production. They need good conditions, being early maturing, with a very good carcase quality. Generally square, meaty, blocky.

Southdown
Ryeland
Dorset Down
Shropshire
Dorset Horn
Wiltshire Horn
Hampshire Down
Suffolk
Oxford

*The longwoolled breeds* – large sheep, suited to good conditions. They grow to a great size, producing plenty of rather coarse meat and a heavy growth of wool. In the past kept for producing mutton from folding on arable crops or good grassland, and today found only in small numbers.

Kent (Romney Marsh)
Leicester
Border Leicester
Wensleydale
Devon & Cornwall Longwoolled
Lincoln

*Cross-breeding* – here rams are mated with ewes of other breeds to produce breeding ewes. These include the Border Leicester, Bluefaced Leicester and Teeswater.

There are several well-known regular crosses:

Scotch half-bred: Border Leicester X Cheviot
Welsh half-bred: Border Leicester X Welsh
Greyface: Border Leicester X Scottish Blackface
Masham: Teeswater X Swaledale
Mule: Bluefaced Leicester X Swaledale (or Scottish
Blackface)

Stratification is geared to the production of plenty of lamb – in numbers, in size, in quick time – for the butcher, then the consumer. The UK's annual per capita lamb consumption is 4.7kg.

Strictly, 'lamb' is sheep in its first year; what ends up in the packet on the supermarket shelf as 'lamb' is often 'hogget', from a sheep in its second year.

Anything slaughtered after first shearing makes for 'mutton'. (Mutton ultimately comes from the Latin *multo*, which was the word for any male sheep. Since the males were more often sent to the slaughter than their milk-producing and lamb-having sisters, the word hopped over to mean 'sheep meat'.) For the last century, mutton has been out of favour and flavour, being stronger in taste than lamb and tougher (because of connective tissue maturation), though it is perhaps making something of a comeback in recent decades; Prince Charles even launched a Mutton Renaissance Campaign in 2004. Such a revival would be particularly good news for raisers of Hebrideans and Shetlands, breeds where the lamb is usually too small for slaughter.

And it is even better news for Hebridean and Shetland lambs themselves.

If you do not eat a sheep at the end of a useful working

life – as conservation grazer, improver of views, spreader of muck, giver of wool – what do you do with it? To send it to the incinerator would be a waste of its life. Let them eat mutton, I say.

~

Whether lamb, hogget or mutton, traditional grass-fed sheep meat is a significant source of dense protein, plus omega-3 fats, CLA (conjugated linoleic acid), vitamin B12 and selenium and niacin. It is also a source of zinc and phosphorus.

Gone, it seems, are the days in the UK when we ate an animal nose to tail. When nothing went to waste. Bones went to soup. Brains went to a 'rissole' with breadcrumbs and eggs. According to the recipe book *The Accomplisht Cook* by Robert May, 1685, the traditional Bride's Pye, the precursor of today's towering wedding cake, contained a filling of oysters, pine kernels, cockscombs, lamb stones, sweetbreads and spices. Sweetbreads are either the thymus (gullet sweetbread) or the pancreas (belly sweetbread). Lamb stones are testicles.

As ruminants, sheep have plenty of stomach – four of them, indeed – thus plenty of material for the sheep 'offal' dish that has withstood fashion and fastidiousness. Scotland's national dish, haggis is a savoury pudding containing sheep's pluck (heart, liver and lungs), minced with onion, oatmeal, suet, spices and salt, mixed with stock, and cooked in casing made from the animal's stomach.

~

A short note on ethical carnivorism, whereby we can have our meat and eat it. This commences with the understanding that the eating of meat from correct sources is a private good, for our health and wellbeing. Beyond this, the public good of eating such meat enables livestock breeds to exist, aids the rural economy, benefits biodiversity, manures the land for the growing of crops. If passenger pigeons had been farmed birds and delicious roasted with rosemary, they would still exist. To appreciate the value of correctly farmed meat on the plate, all schoolchildren at the age of sixteen should witness the slaughter of a cow or a pig or a sheep. An animal's life can only be properly appreciated when its death is witnessed. Meat is more, so much more, than entrecote or chops wrapped in plastic on a Tesco shelf.

The livestock necessary for ethical carnivorism are our native breeds, developed for our climate and habitats, able to thrive without shiploads of imported soya or the vet's constant ministrations. Modern 'commercial' breeds, usually imported, are constitutionally weaker, commercially more expensive to raise. Bring back the old breeds. Slower to grow, perhaps. Less meat, perhaps, but better meat, absolutely.

*Lambs hoping to be invited into the house.*

# THE SEX LIFE OF SHEEP: TUPPING

In autumn, as the days draw in, the sheep's mind and body turn to the thoughts and processes of procreation.

Sheep have been farmed for ten millennia. But the wildness has not left them. The hormonal response to breed, in ram and ewe alike, is dark-started. So, October in the northern hemisphere for almost all sheep breeds, save for a few Mediterranean types, such as the Dorset.

Something else, about October. There tends to be a last rush of grass, to bring the animal to the peak performance. What is distinct about grass is that it grows from the root, not the tip. Consequently, cutting the leaf – whether with teeth, tongue or scythe – causes 'tillering', or new growth. To a degree, the more grass is grazed, the more it grows. On heavy clay soils, such as far western Herefordshire, permanent pasture is a better way of farming, because ploughing and cultivating such land is tricky. It is either too wet to work, or so dry it becomes concrete. And, if tilled, the soil runs away downhill.

A flock of ewes will, by and large, synchronize their reproductive cycle. Most breeds come into season for thirty hours once every seventeen days or so, over a three-month period.

Sheep sex is not pretty. It is rutting. The odour of the oestrous ewe stimulates the ram, who sidles up to her in a low
stretch position with the head angled to the side. Often the ram
bites the flank of the female, flicks his tongue in and out, strikes
her with a stiff foreleg and sniffs the vulva. After contact by the
ram, the ewe usually urinates. The ram then sniffs both vulva
and urine, arches his neck upwards, curls the upper lip to reveal
gums and teeth – the 'flehmen response', which draws odours
over the nasal passage and turbinates. The flehmen response is
believed to facilitate the detection of oestrus.

If the female is receptive she will stand for copulation.

Robin Hood, who bumbled through life, bumbled through
sex. He would climb on the ewe's rear bemusedly, before
falling off. He took at least three mounts before ejaculation,
the ewe beneath stoical. Action Ram serviced first time, every
time. By December he was thin and pale through
fornication.

It can be painful to watch an inexperienced ram mounting.
They have orientation issues.

This is Herbert's first year on the job. He is a two-year-old
Hebridean with promising conformation and as fine a set of
horns as I've ever encountered. Perfect tight, symmetrical
spirals. But for our purposes what suits is his top-of-the-range
tarmac-black fleece.

Since he is junior ram, he waits behind Rammy. Herbert
will re-service mounted ewes, or he will service the ewes
Rammy de-prioritizes. The dominant ram gets first go, first
choice. If Herbert is tempted to a first go, Rammy will inter-
vene. This is no fun for Herbert since, quite aside from being
headbanged, his exposure to the recently mated Rammy
increases his own ardour. Warned off, Herbert goes off to

eat. Higher-ranking males concentrate on courting females when in rut and do not graze to the extent lower-ranking rams do.

Given a choice of breeds to be brides, a ram will invariably choose his own breed over others. Sheep are intensely tribal.

As soon as the ram is satisfied with his servicing, he abandons the ewe. A one-day stand.

A small percentage of rams commonly will not mate with oestrous females and, if given a choice, will display courtship behaviour towards another ram in preference to a female. This partner-preference behaviour of rams may be traceable to foetal development and could represent a phenomenon of sexual differentiation.

Gay rams look like heterosexual rams. Besides, for most of the year the boys hang out together, a sub-flock within the flock, and there tends to be quite a lot of homoerotic play as a matter of course. Only in the rutting season does the gay ram stand out. Our gay ram, Vincent, generally fancied the wethers, the castrated males.

~

In Lower Paddock, the air is thick with the sort of wet that frizzes human hair and clams to a sheep's fleece to give it Swarovski shine. Mutton dressed as princesses.

The brook is in full spate, but even above the roar I can hear the steady clunk-clunk of bone on bone. The usual ratio of ram to ewes is 1 to 25 (higher for a mature ram, more in the region of 1 to 40 ewes). In Lower Paddock there are five Shetland rams and thirty-five Shetland females. Plus wethers. In large groups of sheep or in sheep on large pastures, subordinate rams may achieve mating. In a tightly confined, relatively small band such as this, the social order plays in. The social order is established by horn-clashing and head-banging.

There are five separate jousts proceeding, with groups of rams and wethers standing around to see the outcome. The fighting is not fair – two three-year-old rams, Billy and Bunter, who are friends, are picking on a two-year-old – but it is natural. This is how sheep are in the wild. Sometimes brutal. Mortality in rams is five times that in ewes.

Social rank in sheep does indeed depend on the presence and size of horns, body mass and height at the withers and hocks. To a degree. Badger, so named for his katmoget face-stripe, is actually the *second* biggest Shetland ram in the horn and body departments. So far he has not lost a tournament because his technique is superior. He takes a longer run, meaning more speed.

Bunter, an all-black, is also quick on his feet. Quick in mind too. He is the smallest ram. Sometimes he only pretends to graze; really he is watching for an opportunity to mate. If a senior ram is distracted while mounting – and rivals will try for distractions – he dashes in and services the waiting female. Bunter has always lived on his wits. He was orphaned at less than a week. We could not catch him. He lived by nipping under the ewes and latching on to their teats. Before they realized he was an impostor, he had managed a gulp or two of milk. A street urchin in sheepskin.

Aside from 'naturalism', we keep a variety of Shetland rams because they are differently marked and coloured, produce different lambs.

~

November: air thick with the smoky incense of decaying oak leaves. Sky blue. Rosehips red. A ten-minute trot along the brook, checking fencing. I need to keep Action Ram on my land. A few years ago he climbed some dodgy fencing to impregnate my neighbour Glyn's Welsh Mountain ewes. Glyn was decent about it. Five months later, he went as far as commending Action Ram's progeny, birthed on the mountainside, as 'Very sharp', meaning up on their feet at birth.

Today, a surprise. Behind the stock fence, perched on the bank trying to get *into* the field, are three bright white ewes. Not mine. Not Glyn my neighbour's. These are Welsh Mountains daubed with a blue line across the shoulder. Don't recognize the yellow ear tags, either.

They are ewes in oestrus, in ram-seeking behaviour.

I phone a neighbour, Gerry, who lives across the brook, and leave a message on the phone. 'If you've got three ewes missing, they're in our bottom paddock.'

Gerry Rogers comes around in the afternoon, on his tractor, drops a hundredweight of beets off on the yard as a thank-you, then drives down to the paddock to collect up the ewes in the transport box on the rear of his John Deere. Not your normal farmer, Gerry. He wears glasses and a vague air of scholarly detachment.

'It's their nature,' he says, looking at the three ewes who wandered out looking for sex.

Always good to have the neighbour's sheep stray, of course. Democratizes embarrassment. Glyn's flock have been in our top field for a week.

## Confessions of a Sheepophile II

First time I put a tup in with the flock – if you can call six Jacobs a flock – I presumed that he would cover every ewe without favour. Indiscriminate reproduction. I was wrong. Rameses, the four-horned Jacob ram, had distinct preferences. One Puppy was first. Bledwynn last. Always. Even with sheep on exactly the same reproductive cycle, rams also show some preference for certain females while ignoring others in oestrus.

So, I run two rams with the Hebrideans. Herbert, as well as learning on the job, impregnates the ewes that Rammy rejects.

~

Observations of a shepherd on breeds:

Over twenty-five years, we have kept Jacobs, Ryelands, Shetlands, Hebrideans (and Ryeland X Shetlands, Suffolk/ Shetland X Shetlands).

The Jacobs improved the views, the fleece was modestly profitable, they provided companionable pleasure, but nobody much liked the meat.

No farmer who wants to be taken seriously runs only park animals and primitives, so we ventured into Ryelands, buying ten pedigree sheep from Councillor Morgan in Clehonger, who stuck 50p in the tailgate of the trailer as we towed them away. 'Luck money.' Our Ryelands were pleasingly docile; if they did ever escape they would simply line the lane eating at the verge, and trundle back home behind a bucket of shaken food. Essentially Labradors in sheep's clothing. Less range of personality than Jacobs. A tight-knit flocking mentality. But very hard work on a hill farm, being unhardy. We struggled with them, their feet and stomachs, even on the best, driest grazing.

Our Shetlands have always ticked the boxes. The inherent range of colours and markings makes each individual easily identifiable. The fleece sells, the flesh too. They are intelligent, and characterful. Sufficiently domesticated to be 'in relation' with the farmer, not so over-domesticated – like Texels – that one wonders why scientists bothered cloning Dolly.

Hebrideans. Quite, quite wild, and I struggle to tell one little black sheep from another. (And cannot do so by looks alone; I need to take a reckoning from behaviour.) But profitable. After putting adverts in the *Hereford Times* I've had farmers on the phone offering to double 'the other chap's money'. They sell as park animals, as meat, as fleece, as conservation grazers.

But in truth I like more interaction with my sheep than I can get with Hebrideans, who are always just out of emotional reach. They remain resolutely primitive.

~

My first memory, preserved in saltwater. I am a toddler, strapped in a Silver Cross pushchair, the one with the green canopy to keep out the 1960s sun. My parents (I learn later) are on holiday in Venice, and I am in the care of my great-aunt and great-uncle, Kathy and Willi, who farm sheep at Llangennith on the blustery Gower peninsula, within a pebble's throw of the waves. The pushchair is on the stone flags outside the front door of their white, lime-washed farmhouse. Shadow, Willi's sheepdog, slinks up to the side of the pushchair, levers himself up and peers at me. Before biting me on the face. I was bitten by more than a dog that afternoon, I was bitten by a bug: I have loved dogs and farming ever since.

I'll explain. It was, of course, my fault that Shadow bit me; I had provoked him by waving an ice cream with a 99 chocolate flake in his face. I would have bitten me too. Shadow was my brother – I did not have a human one, or a sister – and on that summer afternoon in the 1960s I learned to treat him like one: with awe. Modern biologists reveal almost monthly that the 'species barrier' between animals and humans is thin; I learned that, Mr Scientist, in my pushchair. I think it was the same afternoon that I saw Shadow flush sheep from the vague ruins of the castle on one word of command from Willi. I held Willi's wind-tanned hand; transmitted through it was the Zen contentment of a man in harmony with his dog, his stock, his land. I wanted the same.

Every evening, I would toddle around with Willi and Shadow to check the ewes, their lambs as brilliant white as the fleecy breakers in the Bristol Channel.

Uncle Willi's Lleyn lambs 'imprinted' on the landscape. They fixed it as home in their heads and staked it as such by scent-marking the ground via the gland in their hooves. They were 'hefted', knew their place by the sight and smell of it. When Willi retired to the inevitable bungalow, the sheep were sold with the farm. In a sense, I imprinted, too. This is when my life in sheep began.

Another memory of Willi, another visit, and just before he retired, so I was about ten. He took me to a livestock market in some small Welsh town (Brecon?), where we sat in stalls in the round, watched sheep being paraded, a pedigree sale of Welsh Mountain sheep, Willi's sheep. He caught the eye of someone in the crowd, grabbed my hand and we went out the back, where Willi met a doppelgänger: a short man with a face as raw as beef under a tweed cap, wearing shepherd's boots (curved upwards at the front, thick heel, to promote a rocking gait). Brief, nervy conversation. Spit on the hand, handshake.

For weeks afterwards I spat into my hand, and said, 'Deal!' On any subject, regarding any question. 'John, do you want macaroni cheese for dinner?' *Ptui*. 'Deal!'

Great-Uncle Willi also introduced me to the term and concept of giving the ram 'the MOT'.

~

Since the best outcome at lambing is reliant on peak sperm production – it takes around seven weeks for sperm to be produced – the rams' testicles need to be checked late summer for size, tone and for lumps.

It is all glamour up on a sheep farm. Under a late summer's amber evening, I have the seven rams penned in the corner of the paddock, separate from their flocks but within sound of them. Keeping low stress.

Action Ram is first for the pre-tupping MOT. I shove him against the gate, loop the halter round his neck, tie him to a bar, then kneel down beside him, facing his rear end. The MOT requires feeling his bollocks, which are dangly and hairy (rather than woolly). Testicles should feel like a firm bicep, and bump-free. In August Action Ram's testicles are sizeable. At peak, late October, they will be enormous and nearly scrape the ground.

My hands go up, down and round his testicles. He stands perfectly still. I actually think he likes having his balls felt.

He gets a pedicure too. Like most domestic sheep the rims of his hooves tend to grow under. He receives my best pedicure, five minutes per foot. He is, after all, going to be spending a lot of time on his back feet.

Regarding the MOT, Action Ram is decidedly unkeen on

what one farming acquaintance calls 'checking the oil with a dipstick'. A thermometer inserted into the rectum. A sheep's body temperature should be about 103°F. Any higher is a cause for concern. Pulse rate, taken inside the hind leg, should be 75–80 per minute.

Ewes also get an MOT. Ewes will normally be two years old before they become a breeding sheep. A ewe coming up to lambing needs to be 'condition scored', rated from 1 (lean) to 5 (fat) by handling. If she is too fat she may not conceive, or have difficulty lambing; too thin and she may not conceive, or produce poor offspring. The ideal number of lambs for a ewe to have differs depending on the farming system. Hill farms prefer ewes to have just one lamb, while sheep in the lowland strive to have twins.

Our primitive breeds need a Goldilocks condition score of 2–2.5. It takes six to eight weeks to lift fat cover by one condition score. That means good grazing if they are scoring below optimum. Good grazing also increases ovulation.

I am always on the hunt for good grazing. Like a sheep.

~

My parents – before they finally divorced – bought me my own Welsh collie sheepdog, and in honour of Uncle Willi's dog I called him Shadow. It is also a classic sheepdog name, consisting of two syllables as recommended two millennia ago by the Roman writer Columella (AD 4–70) in *De Re Rustica* (On Agriculture):

> Dogs should be called by names which are not very long, so that each may obey more quickly when he is called, but they should not have shorter names than those which are pronounced in two syllables, such as the Greek Σκύλαξ (puppy) and the Latin

Ferox (savage), the Greek Λάκων (Spartan) and the Latin Celer (speedy) or, for a bitch, the Greek Σπουδή (zeal), Ἀλκή (Valour), Ῥωμή (strength) or the Latin Lupa (she-wolf), Cerva (hind) and Tigris (tigress).

Both Shadows had one blue eye, one brown eye.

It was a mistake to give me Shadow. We had no sheep, and he wanted to work. So he rounded up everything he espied. Small children. Tortoises. Postmen.

In boredom and frustration, Shadow ate my mother's daffodils, at which point she decreed he had to leave. He went off to a farm by Aconbury. (I visited him once. I was sad for me, happy for him: he had plenty of sheep to supervise.) My mother went off also.

My father bought me a golden Labrador Retriever.

One does not have to be a Jungian psychologist to see that the above may have caused some ambiguity regarding sheep dogs. I have never worked sheep with one. But one day I might.

~

Sheep respond to a dog as if it were a predator. There are two main types of collie sheepdog: those that fix the flock with a stare and dominate by force of will, and the more active type that runs about a lot, and barks.

Both Shadows were hyper-active.

The derivation of 'collie' is beclouded. The usual cited origin is 'coaly', meaning black, which swerves the inconvenient obstacle that few collies are totally sooty. Most have white or tan markings as well. The more compelling explanation, and that suggested by Philip Walling in *Counting Sheep*, is that 'collie' is derived from the tongue of the Celts. He notes that *Coelio,* in the Brythonic language of the Celtic peoples of Wales, southern Scotland and the north of England, 'means *to trust* or *be faithful* to'. In additional proof, in the Isle of Man the word for sheepdog is *coly* – same root. The contemporary Border collie is almost entirely descended from Old Hemp, a dog bred in 1893 by Adam Telfer in Northumberland. Telfer said of Old Hemp, 'He flashed like a meteor across the sheepdog horizon. There never was such an outstanding personality.'

On Uncle Willi's knee, I learned about drovers' dogs, because his father could remember as a boy the sheep being rounded up on the Gower for the long march to an English livestock market. This, before the railways. Apparently, the drovers, on reaching their destination, would get a stagecoach home, and rather than pay for the dog to travel, assume it could find its own way. One dog, Carlo, allegedly travelled over 200 miles from London to West Wales all by himself. He had memorized the landscape. Publicans gave him a bite of bread and cheese and sip of beer to help him on his way.

I suppose, too, that another reason I have eschewed sheepdogs is that so many of my fellow farmers have problems with theirs.

## Confessions of a Sheepophile III

Last year Action Ram – half Suffolk, half Shetland – bulldozed the fence to allow himself access to our pure breed Hebridean flock. We were away. He impregnated every single one of them. It is possible to siphon out ram semen from ewe vaginas but there are limits.

Looking over the sheep now as they graze in Bank Field

(our predecessors did not waste energy on nomenclature: our field names include Road Field), the flock is an embarrassment of shades and sizes. The products of the ovine miscegenation must go. We'll be laughing stock for our livestock.

I place an advertisement in the *Hereford Times* classifieds: 'Fifty cross-breed lambs and hoggets. Offers.'

The ad comes out on Thursday and that evening a dealer called Ian Maund phones, sounds me out and arranges to come around eleven on Sunday morning to look the sheep over. If he likes them, he'll take them there and then.

'Do you have a dog?' I ask, thinking this might save me penning them.

'Oh aye, I've got a dog. I'll bring him all right.'

At thirty minutes past eleven on Sunday a large Nissan pick-up rattles into the yard. Behind the Nissan is a trailer with the painted legend: *Ian P Maund. Cattle dealer and stores.* Rangy, smiling, a fellow forty-something, Ian Maund hops out.

So do his two young sons. I compliment Ian Maund on his shiny Ifor Williams aluminium stock trailer. 'Nice trailer, by the way. What is it, twin-deck?'

'Single-deck, but it's got interior doors.'

There are few things farmers like more than discussing kit. I know some who buy the 'journals', the trade magazines, just to look at the pictures.

Penny, Tris, Freda, and Ian's two boys, Nat and James, sigh.

'Right then, better go and look at these sheep,' says Ian, assuming a business-like air. 'I'll get the dog.' He disappears round the back of the pick-up and reappears with a young collie sheepdog, quivering with excitement, on a lead. 'Shall I let him go, Nat?'

'No! Don't do that, Dad, he'll run off.'

A sheepdog that runs off? Such is the first portent of the disaster that is to come.

'What's the dog's name?' I ask Nat.

'Rocky.'

Rocky, straining on his leash, leads the party down the yard into the fields below the house.

The bottom three fields are interconnected, with no real fencing between them, but it is the work of only moments to interrupt the sheep and move them baaing to the topmost field. All the while Ian's looking the sheep over; I'm not expecting a fortune and Ian's not offering it.

We agree a price for the lot and shake hands. All that remains is to pen the sheep. Ian walks across to the middle of the field where Nat is standing patiently with the impatient Rocky.

Holding Rocky's head between his hands, Ian looks into Rocky's eyes. 'Now listen to me, Rocky, you're going to be a good dog and pen the sheep,' says Ian, pointing at the sheep and the corner pen fifty yards from them.

I am severely impressed by this pre-programming of Rocky. So is Rocky. Unleashed, he rockets to the startled sheep, snaps at their heels and starts bringing them across towards the pen. 'That's it, Rocky! Bring 'em on!'

It is at this point that Rocky decides that shepherding sheep is not half as much fun as chasing them. He darts to the middle of the tight flock, snapping and barking and jumping. The flock explodes in all directions, like someone dropping a hand grenade in a bale of cotton. 'Rocky! Bloody get here or I'll warm your arse!' bellows Ian in a voice that echoes down the valley clear to Pandy six miles away.

Rocky, not liking Ian's attitude, decides to run up to Freda to say hello. Followed by a licky greeting to me, to Penny, to Tris, before James grabs him by the collar. We all troop down to Copse Field, spread out in a line and drive the straggled pockets of sheep back up again.

The kids are quietly enjoying themselves. I am getting hot with the walking.

'To think,' I say to Ian, 'some lucky sods are still in bed this morning and not chasing bloody sheep.'

'Ah,' says Ian. 'Poor them, I say, on a glorious morning like this.'

At the top of Bog Field, Rocky is once again sent off on his penning errand, with a startlingly similar result to the first time. 'Rocky, you bastard! I'll warm your arse for you.' We go back down, drive the sheep up . . .

After Rocky's fourth failed attempt at penning the sheep I go and get a bucket of sheep nuts and stand, somewhat embarrassed, by the pen and shout, 'Sheep! Sheep!' The tamest sheep come running to the lure and follow me into the pen, and I quickly close the gate. About eleven are in.

After an hour I've got all the sheep in save for seven refuseniks who won't come close. It is then that Rocky finally does some penning. Nat puts him on a lead and, tugging him, runs up and down behind the sheep. The sheep, startled by this strange conjoined animal, bolt and join their companions in the pen. I run in behind them and drag the last gate closed. I look at my watch. We've been rounding up the sheep for three hours. Nat and Rocky walk up. Rocky looks at the sheep and barks proudly.

Noise carries a long way in a remote, narrow V-shaped valley. Everyone I bumped into in the village shop for the next month asked about the state of Rocky's arse.

My fault of course. I had not yet understood the nature of primitive sheep. I should never have let a collie near them.

Sheepdogs do not only have to be trained. You have to have the right sheep to train the sheepdog on. Which are not Hebridean crosses.

～

If you own a mountain, I see the need for a sheepdog. As shepherd James Hogg wrote in 1809:

A single shepherd and his dog will accomplish more in gathering a stock of sheep from a Highland farm than twenty shepherds could without dogs, and it is a fact that without this docile animal the pastoral life would be a blank. Without the shepherd's dog the whole of the open mountainous land in Scotland would not be worth a sixpence. It would require more hands to manage a stock of sheep, gather them from the hills, force them into houses and folds, and drive them to markets, than the profits of the whole stock were capable of maintaining.

We are on a hill farm – subtly different – with hedges and fence. Easier to train the sheep to the bucket, particularly if they are sheep that will not flock.

I may not use a sheep dog on our sheep, but I do use a dog.

～

Strange to say, a dog taught to retrieve makes a useful faux-sheepdog (it can be sent about to sit and block escape routes) and I drive the hundred and twenty sheep easily into the pens under the alders, on which the leaves are still clinging to life. Like the oak, the alder comes into leaf late, and defoliates late. It is all change down on the farm in October. The wind has blown away the last straggling hirondelles; the self-same wind from the north brought the first redwings on its back edge. Thus the scene is replenished with birds. Some of our sheep are also migrating. October is traditionally a month of sheep sales, so I spend the morning sifting and sorting the ewes, the lambs, the hoggets, the surplus wethers. This little sheepy will go to Tenbury Wells market, this little sheepy will stay at home. Almost all the money in sheep farming is made in the months of September and October. At eleven there is disco-shimmering drizzle; by twelve it is raining properly, and the leaves of the alders are no shelter at all.

The rain does nothing to dampen the ardour of the five tups, who spend their hours in captivity trying to climb the galvanized hurdles to get at the ewes. The ewes are on heat. Under the low canopy of the alder the greasy musk of the aroused rams smothers like a foul cloud.

Down in the dingle the buck deer are barking. It is the rutting season for them too. They are close relations of sheep.

~

Lambs are born around 147 days after the ewe falls pregnant. Being poor at maths, my rule of thumb is that a ewe mounted on 5 November will lamb around 1 April. Most lambs in a flock are born within a six-week period (two cycles of ovine ovulation), and nearly all Britain's ewes will have lambed by the end of April. And so the cycle of sheep and shepherding restarts.

~

Action Ram died in mysterious circumstances. A neighbour's flock broke into one of our fields. The neighbour rounded up his sheep but, being unable to get Action Ram off the back of a ewe, took him too, promising to return him next day. It was late.

On the following morning, my neighbour's white Hilux pulled up on the yard. He lifted the tailgate, and there was Action Ram, dead.

'I put him in the stable last night . . . and this morning he was like this.'

Action Ram may have broken his head trying to break out. He may have died of stress. He hated being alone. He was a sheep.

Dishonourably, there was part of me that was relieved he was dead. Tupping time stressed me because he was impossible to contain. He had the big Suffolk body and the athleticism and intelligence of a Shetland. I had to patrol a mile's worth of fences, at least twice daily, between October and December. I felt like a border guard. Or perhaps a prison one.

I miss him though.

V

# THE WAY SHEEP DIE: DEATH, SLAUGHTER, DISEASE AND POLITICS

### SHEEP IN WINTER

*The sheep get up and make their many tracks*
*And bear a load of snow upon their backs,*
*And gnaw the frozen turnip to the ground*
*With sharp quick bite, and then go noising round*
*The boy that pecks the turnips all the day*
*And knocks his hands to keep the cold away*
*And laps his legs in straw to keep them warm*
*And hides behind the hedges from the storm.*
*The sheep, as tame as dogs, go where he goes*
*And try to shake their fleeces from the snows.*
*Then leave their frozen meal and wander round*
*The stubble stack that stands beside the ground,*
*And lie all night and face the drizzling storm*
*And shun the hovel where they might be warm.*

JOHN CLARE

Farming, eh? As my grandfather used to say, 'It's nothing but crisis management.' Actually he tended to mutter, 'It's one bloody thing after another,' before excusing himself with, 'Pardon my French.' Poppop did sixty years down on the farm.

Today began well, so I should have known it could only get worse. Around 3 p.m. I go to check the sheep in the bottom meadow. A mist spews out of the dingle, where all the mists of the world are made. There is a certain comedy in counting white sheep in mist. But there is nothing funny about realizing that a ram is missing. I find him hanging upside down on the stock fence. He'd climbed over it, then on the dismount trapped his rear legs in the wire strands. The grass in the other field was no greener.

He is panting, and foam-mouthed. I sprint back to the house, grab the fencing pliers and, from the gun-safe, the Lincoln 12-bore.

I cut the ram down, trying to hold his body against me so he does not fall.

Slabbed on his side, I stroke his muzzle. There is no hope; his back is broken. I say soothing things, false things, and place the merciful shotgun behind his head.

After the blast, only a marble string of skin remains connecting head to body. On the meat shelf of the supermarket, blood is dull and ochre in its plastic wrapping. Fresh blood is strangely fluorescent. As it spreads over the thin grass, it is the only bright thing in the afternoon.

The ram was Snowy, a white Shetland.

Do sheep feel pain? They do. I know because I look into their eyes as they die.

One way or another, I have seen a lot of sheep die.

~

1999. I have arranged for Kev the butcher from Grosmont to slaughter four Jacob ram lambs. Sheep farming is a long exercise in Sod's Law; I had wanted girl lambs from our two best Jacob ewes, Bledwynn and One Puppy, because they sell for more, especially when you have a pedigree family tree which stretches back to the Ark, as Bled and One Puppy do. Naturally, they had sprung two boy lambs each. There is little sell-on market for Jacob ram lambs as sires.

The due day for dispatch arrives; it is one of those sunny September afternoons that make you think summer may never end. I pen the four rams beside the stock trailer at the very top of Cwm Field; the view over the Golden Valley is a pastorally perfect quilt of meadows and cornfields on gently swelling hills.

The rams are alert, but relaxed; standing still, not milling or climbing the metal hurdles that encase them. Being penned is just a fact of life for the rams, a chore to be endured; in their six months of life they have been penned for ear tagging, feet cleaning, dagging.

So the lambs are relaxed; I look into the eyes of each one, to remind myself of their value and their beauty. And they are gorgeous: spotted black and white, their tight curly wool gleaming, their horns curling in geometrically exact spirals.

Kevin drives up in his Toyota Land-Cruiser, towing the galvanized trailer on which the cadavers will be hung. The butcher's hooks carry on rattling when the Toyota stops. Kevin and his new assistant Tom have had a busy day; their white coats are smeared in blood. They look like wandering extras from *The Texas Chainsaw Massacre*. Tom cannot get over how handsome the rams look. He keeps rubbing his red stubble, saying, 'Kev, look at them!' It is Tom's second day on the job. He's in his mid-twenties, and has the grey pallor of someone who has spent too much time smoking roll-ups, making a pint last an afternoon down the Dog at Ewyas Harold.

Kev the Butcher, a man of few words, wordlessly hands the new boy the black .45 revolver that is the killing tool.

I confess the next seconds are shards of picture, rather than a complete portrait. Tom leans over into the pen, puts the revolver against the forehead of the nearest ram and pulls the trigger.

*BANG!* The bullet ricochets off the ram's head to *PING!* against the metal wall of the trailer.

The ram is entirely unmoved, and wholly alive. Kev crosses his arms. 'Nah. Try again.'

Another shot, another ricochet, another failure. I have now dived behind the end of the stock trailer, so I can only hear what happens next.

'Fucking 'ell, give it to me.'

Four rapid shots, the thud of four bodies collapsing.

Silence. Reassuring silence.

I stand up, brush the sheep shit off the front of my overalls.

The butchers are pulling the bodies of the rams out to hang them up for gutting and skinning.

Kev looks at me and raises his eyes to Heaven. 'Back of the head with a sheep, back of the head.'

I dine out on this story a lot. I can say truthfully that I have been under fire, heard the drone – quite like a bee's flight – of a bullet past my head.

~

My views on sheep have changed a lot since that afternoon decades ago. I would, for instance, no longer have lambs slaughtered for meat. I will, however, defend sheep, and sheep farming, together with the on-farm slaughter of (mature) sheep. The apprentice bungled that afternoon, but it was the right way for a sheep to die, in the right place – which is its home.

Today it is compulsory for all animals entering the food chain to be slaughtered at a licensed abattoir. The number of abattoirs is insufficient, however, meaning that animals have a long trip, packed tight in a trailer to the slaughterhouse.

Stress, as well as being cruel to the sheep, produces excesses of lactic acid, meaning the meat becomes ill-flavoured.

Frequently, the animals sense their destiny at the abattoir and struggle to escape. To persuade sheep into the killing chamber, slaughterhouses use a trained 'Judas sheep' to entice them forwards.

On-farm slaughter has the singular advantage that the sheep are less stressed before death. The next time the apprentice came, the excess rams were eating beet pellets as happy as Larry the Lamb. The shooting was so quick that the four were all mid-munch when they dropped dead, all in a row.

I would not mind going the same way.

Britons eat 306,000 tonnes of sheep meat each year. This equates to approximately 1,041,000 sheep killed per month.

~

*Ethical carnivorism: a short proposal note on the humane killing of sheep.* Sheep deserve a decent death, and there should be no more stressful, long-distance transport to a fear-reeking abattoir. 'On-spot slaughtering' by high-velocity rifle has been successfully campaigned for in Switzerland by animal welfare association Four Paws (*Vier Pfoten Schweiz*). This method is already used in UK for 'farmed' deer. At the very least mobile abattoirs need to be reintroduced into Britain; a number of countries within the EU, as well as Canada, New Zealand and America, have such mobile facilities operating within tight regulatory frameworks that are good for biosecurity and animal welfare (see Sustainable Food Trust, *A Good Life and a Good Death*, 2018).

~

Sheep die from disease, as well as slaughter and Snowy-sort accidents. Sheep are tormented by a long list of diseases: sheep scab (where a mite gets under the skin and causes intense irritation), foot rot, orf (exanthematous disease caused by a parapox virus, transmissible to humans), liver fluke, botulism, black leg, braxy, enzootic posthitis and vulvitis (pizzle rot), enzootic abortion of ewes (EAE) . . .

My memories of the Foot-and-Mouth epidemic of 2001 lie in fragments of film. Clippings on the floor. We chained and padlocked our gates to prevent anyone coming on the property . . . One morning I walked up the hill behind the house, and we were surrounded by smoking pyres of animals being burned, and the barbecue stench filled the air . . . Buckets of disinfectant . . . Troops with rifles in a Land Rover going up the lane . . . The wheels and the underside of the trailer being sprayed at Hereford market by men in those plastic suits forensic pathologists wear . . . Talking to Peter Jinman, the vet on the lane, the gate to the house open, and Lollipop – who lived in the orchard – coming through to see us, Jinman quipping, 'Unauthorized sheep movement!' . . . Paperwork, paperwork, if you ever could move livestock given the restriction orders . . . A neighbour having his flock slaughtered in 'a contagious cull', the idea being to create a buffer zone between the disease and the healthy stock. A cordon sanitaire. We lived in fear for our animals' lives.

False sentiment, given that they would normally go the way of all sheep flesh, to die for us? I do not think so. Some were pets (Lollipop was in this category, Action Ram almost), some were friends (Robin Hood, Sooty), some were pedigree breeding stock (thus useful for the continuation of the breed), some because they were rare or helping preserve genetic diversity, and all had a life worth living for five good years at least. All had worth, function, purpose. A role to play in our lives, and the life of Nature.

Foot-and-Mouth was a panic. Most of the six million cloven-hooved animals culled were needlessly killed because we humans ran around in a lather. Like putative sheep. So, sense and compassion went up in smoke, along with millions of animals and billions of pounds sterling, and Britain's green and pleasant land was turned into killing fields.

It need not have happened. The Netherlands also had an outbreak of FMD in 2001. It was brought under control by mass vaccination.

~

There is an old farming adage 'A sheep's worst enemy is a sheep'. As with most folky rural sayings, it contains a nugget of truth. Many sheep together on the same ground for too long a time builds up the burden of gastrointestinal worms. The common result – aside from loss of condition, leading to susceptibility to a host of other diseases ovines are prone to – is that the sheep's back end becomes soiled by 'scours' (diarrhoea). Too much lush grass produces the same result.

Scours attract blowflies, which lay their eggs on the sheep's wool. The eggs hatch into maggots, which begin to gorge on dead skin, then live flesh. Once the maggot feeding frenzy starts, the smell (somewhere between piss in a stairwell and damp in a cellar) attracts more flies.

During the early stages of flystrike the afflicted sheep becomes mildly restless, sitting down and standing up. Within a day it starts stretching its neck backwards and nibbling at its back end. Soon the fleece hangs off in long strips that come away in the hand, and along its back and flanks is a seething mass of maggots. In the terminal stages, its will broken, the sheep will leave the flock and die.

I confess: in twenty-five years I have 'lost' three sheep to fly-strike, having failed to see the dark tell-tale stain of maggot excretion under black fleece. I had applied an organic-approved anti-fly pour-on but it had clearly come to the end of its efficacy.

One way or another, sheep require constant vigilance. I was insufficiently watchful over my flock.

~

For balance, my best James Herriot moment: a fat Ryeland fell in the brook, evidently managed to scramble out and up the bank before becoming 'cast', having rolled on her back and being unable to stand because of the weight of wet fleece. And because she was 'cast' she was unable to belch gas from her rumen, and developed 'bloat'. When I found her under June sunshine she was swelling like a balloon and minutes from death. I stabbed her in the side with a pen knife. She deflated, and walked off.

~

Most of the catalogue of diseases sheep are prone to do not affect wild sheep. Or sheep in extensive (low stocking rate)

systems, with closed flocks in a natural ovine society, on a grass-
and browse-based organic and varied diet. Like ours.

In twenty-five years we have had, in addition to the blowfly
victims, five sheep die from barber's pole (unlucky), five culled
due to contracting orf (from a sick stray sheep that broke in),
and five or so in which the cause of death was undetermined.
Why the low incidence? In addition to all the above, because
we have primitive breeds.

Selective breeding of sheep began with Jacob in the Bible.
There is nothing inherently wrong with selective breeding.
Every farmer does it to a degree. But by Cuvier's Law of Cor-
relation one gain is offset by a loss. Bakewell knew that a sheep's
carcase could not be changed without its wool deteriorating,
because to improve the one necessarily causes the other to
deteriorate. The story of modern sheep farming is that the con-
stitution of sheep has diminished as their market meatiness has
grown. Modern 'commercial' breeds are simply less tough.

The answer is back to the future. Bring back the old breeds.
Less meat, but better meat.

~

At university I read History, and for some years afterwards,
before returning home to Herefordshire, worked as an histor-
ical researcher. I attribute to my acquaintance with history the
cause of my scepticism concerning the religious certainties of
science (which change every epoch, but are always held fer-
vently) and any notion that society is on an entirely upwards
course.

Take veterinary medicine, which became commonplace
under the Romans. (The Latin for 'animal doctor' is *veterinar-
ius*, as patented by Columella, who wrote twelve volumes on

agriculture and animal husbandry *c.* AD 42–68.) Prescriptions by Roman wise men like Columella and Cato would be used in farmyards until medieval times. When the Western Roman Empire fell to the barbarians in 476, veterinary medicine entered a Dark Age. Although the countryside of Europe swarmed with self-proclaimed animal healers, from 'cow-leeches' (who tended sheep as well as bovines) to 'hoggelders', the standard of their practice was epitomized by a medieval cure for constipation in oxen: 'A lively trout ... was taken from the adjoining stream, and committed to the gullet of the patient, under the assurance that it would soon work its way through all impediments, and speedy relief be afforded.'

Neither the ox nor the fish survived. If the 'scientific' cow-leech failed, God, spells, astrology and charms were invoked. The most fortunate beasts in medieval times were those left untreated, since other veterinary treatments included being bled and being burned.

The Dark Ages were a step back from Columella's advice on sheep scab: apply olive oil, which contains oleocanthal, an anti-inflammatory drug. But modern veterinary science is not all shining light. Take current thinking about scrapie.

Scrapie has been a catalogued incurable malady of sheep and goats for over three hundred years and likely been endemic for as long as humanity has shepherded ovines. The disease is recorded as massacring flocks of Norfolk Horns on the Cambridgeshire heaths in the eighteenth century; it is called scrapie because affected sheep scrape themselves against solid objects in order to rid themselves of the maddening itching.

Like BSE in cattle, scrapie is one of those diseases collectively referred to as 'transmissible spongiform encephalopathy' (TSE).

The world expert on TSEs is Stanley Prusiner from the University of California; in 1982 he discovered a minuscule protein on cells of the spleen, and the nervous and lymphatic systems. He termed this protein a prion (a condensing of 'proteinaceous infectious particle') and noted that in all TSE-infected animals such prions were deformed. Thus, he concluded, deformed prions are the cause of neuro-degenerative diseases, including scrapie. Prions are resistant to all the standard disinfectants – ultraviolet, radiation, formalin. They persist so long in soil that burying does not destroy them, which is one reason why farmers now are prevented from interring dead livestock on their own land.

As a result of Prusiner's ideas, hundreds of thousands of sheep have been killed and incinerated, despite the animals being disease-free: these sheep were merely judged to be statistically at risk. And the risk was assessed by comparing the genetic codes of 1,500 'scrapie' sheep with the genetic codes of 14,000 unaffected sheep. But animal malady matters are rarely clear cut, a convenient black and white: in some countries where sheep have 'putative infectious prion' (PrP) in the genetic code there is no scrapie. Neither, it transpires, is there one scrapie, but twenty or more variants. More: high-risk sheep do not necessarily develop the disease, even if born to mothers with the symptoms of the disease.

~

In France, on holiday, I read in *Sud Ouest* newspaper an article detailing a project to build 'medicinal' hedges for horses, on which they could self-medicate. This is the new, bright white thinking.

Translate: humans have finally understood what animals and peasant farmers have known for a very long time. The beasts know best. That is why wild animals live healthy lives.

~

One environmental case against sheep is that they have 'sheep-wrecked' Britain. In the words of the *Guardian* columnist George Monbiot:

> I have an unhealthy obsession with sheep. It occupies many of my waking hours; it haunts my dreams. I hate them. Perhaps I should clarify that statement. I hate not the animals themselves, which cannot be blamed for what they do, but their impact on both our ecology and our social history. Sheep are the primary reason – closely followed by grouse shooting and deer stalking – for the sad state of the British uplands. Partly as a result of their assaults, Wales now possesses less than one third of the average forest cover of Europe. Their husbandry is the greatest obstacle to the rewilding I would like to see.

Again:

> Overwhelmingly the reason [for ecological holocaust] is farming: grazing which prevents woods from regenerating and destroys the places where animals and plants might live.

In other words, the only landscape worth a jot is one rewilded with trees, trees, trees. But, surely, my hay meadow, with thirty plant species per metre, with skylarks nesting, with foxes stalking rabbits, is also a place where 'animals and plants might live'? The meadow grazed by sheep for part of the year, the grass (and flower) crop which make their winter feed.

I really do like trees. I have planted them, and I have managed a wood. On my real trophy shelf, I have an award from a woodland charity for my books on oaks and woods. But we need a diversity of wildlife-rich habitats. Such as grassland land for *meadow* pipits and *meadowsweet*, and arable fields for *corn* marigold and *corn* buntings.

Treeland is not the only habitat.

~

I used to be weary from farming sheep. Now I am wearied by mad-dog political attacks on sheep.

People can be very disdainful about domesticated farm animals. To rid Britain of sheep would entail the extinction of ovine breeds hundreds, sometimes thousands, of years old.

They kill sheep, don't they, the rewilders.

And here is the funny thing. The proper husbandry of livestock, including sheep, is a great aid to managing woodland for wildlife.

~

Into the December wood, the trees baubled with stars. A long day, and I have not checked the sheep here yet.

When we took over Cockshutt, the ground level was a monoculture of bramble. As with everything in the countryside one needs moderation and multi-agriculture. Some bramble is good (cover for hares, rabbits, pheasants etc.); an entire flooring of bramble is bad (no grassy glades for wildflowers).

To clear the bramble I could have used a noisy, man-made, fume-emitting petrol brush-cutter. Instead, I have used thirty Hebridean sheep in areas designated by my temporary stock fencing.

I shine the torch around. Jesus. They really are good at their brush-clearance job, Hebrideans. The glade, about a quarter of an acre, looks as though a giant hand has swiped it. Ground Zero. As well as eating the bramble leaves – brambles being surprisingly evergreen for a deciduous plant – they have even tackled the thorny stems. (Deer use bramble leaves as hard tack in winter.)

The sheep's eyes glitter like green emeralds in the light of the torch. They are camped together, most facing west, but a few sentinels watch out for the wolves of sheep nightmares. Two, on hearing my approach, stir and stand, rising on the knuckles of the front legs.

I call 'Sheep! Sheep!' to greet them, to reassure them.

They recognize my voice. All rise, and come flocking towards me, Hilda at the tip of the wool arrow, as always. (Memo: Hebrideans do not flock for danger, but do for food.) On my shoulder, a bale of sweet meadow hay for their hay rack. Their justified dessert after their laborious main course.

At the top of the wood, which is mainly composed of oak and ash, up towards Garway Hill the resident male tawny, Old Brown, hoots.

Next afternoon. About 2 p.m. Unseemly warm for December. I've taken a bow saw to a batch of hazels I'm 'coppicing' (cutting down to stumps, to promote regrowth, and while they regrow to allow in the light). The sawn-off branches I lob over the netting to the Hebrideans, who peel off the bark of the younger stuff, as quick as I can supply it. Free food for sheep. The shepherd's delight.

This is almost next to their bedding site, already a mat of knobbly black 'crot'. Where there is muck there is insect life. Where there is insect life, there are reptiles, mammals and birds in an ascending food chain. Over the last years, the resident tawny owls have increased their clutch size by 200 per cent, a reliable indicator of improved and increased diet. We have more warblers in the wood. How come? Because of management – and the insects attracted by the dung from the sheep and the cows run through the place from time to time. In summer the shit of the sheep and cows runs with flies, and is mined by dung beetles.

Where there's livestock muck there's a wealth of invertebrate life. Of the fifty-six British Red Data Book species of beetle associated with dung, thirteen live in sheep excrement.

~

Conventionally, gastrointestinal parasites in sheep are controlled by anthelmintics. Many of the chemicals in the 'wormer' are excreted as surplus in the faeces, largely unmetabolized, where they cause mortality in dung beetles. This is killing the shepherd's little helpers: dung-colonizing insect communities in temperate climates, which mainly include small endocoprid dung beetles in the genus Aphodius, will reduce the development and survival of livestock gastrointestinal parasites on pastures over the summer grazing season. Thus:

The conservation of dung beetles in temperate climates is therefore important in livestock management, not only for their role in dung degradation and nutrient cycling, but because they can contribute to the reduction in abundance of economically deleterious gastrointestinal parasites. Livestock management practices should focus on reducing reliance on anthelmintics to minimise damage to natural dung beetle populations.*

Or, Nature balances Nature, if you let it. And farm sustainably.

~

My own personal extinction rebellion. Why do so few care about the sheep breeds that have disappeared off the face of the Earth as decidedly as the Dodo? Such as the Scottish Dunface.

I have decided to eat more meat from our remaining native and rare breeds to do my bit to help preserve them. (See Appendix.)

~

In Tudor times, when my family started farming sheep (as opposed to stealing them), there were as many baa-baas in the Welsh Borders as now. It sang with wildflowers, was lit by birdsong then. With sheep.

It's not the sheep, stupid. It is the way they are farmed today.

~

I sometimes get asked to attend literary festivals. Sheep/rewilding has become thrust up the question list, and I've lost count of the #meatfree campaigners who've told me that all we need to

---

\* Sands and Wall, *Journal of Applied Ecology* (see bibliography)

do to make food production sustainable is to stop eating meat. Really? What about the environmental cost of palm oil, soya bean oil, rape oil?

~

Pro-environment uses of a sheep, Number 28:

You learn through experience, through trying things out. We run our sheep on a grass-fed system. They get about 95 per cent of their food from either fresh grass, preserved grass (hay) or browse. The other 5 per cent is from cereal-based concentrate, used as a winter warmer, health-enhancer, and mostly to tame them by rattling it in a bucket. Grass is basic everyday fodder. Concentrate is a treat. Worth running for.

But organic concentrate is expensive. So a few years ago, I decided to grow my own wheat in a trial. How to nourish the land on which the wheat crop was to be sown? I 'folded' sheep, whose manure enriched the dull clay. The wheat grown – a heritage variety – fed the sheep which had manured the same ground. A virtuous circle, well known to farmers as long ago as the Stone Age, which really does work.

Since I used no inorganic chemicals on the said ground, the wildlife bloomed.

~

Sheep are implicated in climate change, but the case against them and other ruminants is sometimes hot air.

First, agriculture contributes just 10 per cent of the UK's carbon emissions, whereas transport contributes 26 per cent and energy 25 per cent. Ruminants also only recycle carbon recently photosynthesized from the atmosphere by the plants they eat.

Second, 71 per cent of UK farmland is under grass, most of

this for sound agronomic and environmental reasons, in that it is either too steep, too acid, too stony for crop production, or is to be kept as permanent pasture due to its botanical diversity and benisons for pollinators and small mammals. If this land were not grazed, most of it would not produce food in future, leaving as the only solutions the intensification of agriculture on the remaining land or production 'offshore' – that is, grow the sheep/cattle elsewhere in the world and import them. With all the Greenhouse Gas (GHG) negatives of transportation. Or starve. Grassland, it might be noted, stores as much.[*]

Third, the furore around ruminants 'burping' methane is partly caused by bad methodology. The UN's report *Livestock's Long Shadow* claimed livestock are responsible for 18 per cent of GHG emissions – but the figure included emissions along the entire supply chain, from land use to processing and refrigeration in supermarkets. The same calculation should apply to non-meat production. To its equal detriment.

Fourth, there is a lack of understanding about the methane emitted in sheeps' burps, and how it acts in the environment. While methane is twenty-eight times more heat-trapping than carbon dioxide, methane's lifespan is just a decade. The global methane budget shows that almost all of the methane produced each year – including the 188 metric tons from livestock – is also broken down each year.[†] If no new animals are added to the system, then the methane toll will not rise.

Fifth, sheep enable an elimination of synthetic nitrogen, on which crop production in farming systems without livestock is

---

[*]   See, for example, Tara Garnett et al., *Grazed and Confused*, University of Oxford, 2017.

[†]   Source: Global Carbon Project.

crucially dependent. Nitrogen fertilizer, among other polluting downers, causes the release of nitrous oxide ... one of the fundamental greenhouse gases responsible for global warming. Added to synthetic nitrogen's long shadow must be the costs of its production, and transportation.

Sixth, not all sheep-rearing systems are the same. Organic ruminant production provides lower-emission footprints than conventional systems.*

Seventh, climate change is far from being the only problem facing humanity. The intensive arable (crop) areas of Britain, some of which lose tons of top soil per acre per annum, are running out of fertility.[†] Even *The Farmer's Guardian*, not noted for alarmism, says that British arable land is in 'crisis'. The picture is similar across the world.

And what better way to restore soil fertility than to include sheep on grass in a rotational system of crop production? The sheep: the original, natural fertilizer of soil.

~

The indispensable William Youatt on sheep shit:

> Sheep's dung is valuable for manure, and for some other purposes. It has been supposed, and probably with truth, that it contributes more to the improvement of the land than does the

---

* See Lynch, J., Garnett, T., Persson, M., Röös, E. and Reisinger, A., *Methane and the Sustainability of Ruminant Livestock* (Foodsource: building blocks), Food Climate Research Network, University of Oxford, 2020.

† P. Panagos et al. in *Environmental Science and Policy* 124, 2021, give a baseline loss of 3.07 tonnes of soil per hectare of agricultural land in the UK and EU.

dung of cattle. It contains a greater proportion of animal matter, and that condensed into a smaller compass; and it falls upon
the ground in a form and manner more likely to be trodden
into and incorporated with it, than the dung of cattle. Hence
arose the system of folding sheep on the arable part of a farm in
many districts in the midland and southern parts of England.
The sheep were penned on a small space of ground, and the
pens being daily shifted, a considerable quantity of land was
ultimately manured.

~

As I neared the dead Hebridean, I failed to notice the crow on
its head, but, in fairness, they were a colour match. Black on
black. Then I saw the crow, and saw it was stabbing. So tempt-
ing is eye of sheep the crow did not desist pecking, despite the
approaching car. Stupidly, I parked the Jeep nose into the wind,
which made opening the door impossible, so I had to turn it
round. The extra minute was all the time the crow needed to
finish its crude dissection, and as I opened the car door with
wind-assist, the crow flew, the delicacy of sheep's eye in its
beak.

The head was arched back, as though its final moment had
been protest or prayer to Heaven. Sheep usually go to cover to
die; they hope for safety from predators, but their sanctuary is
their graveyard. My little Hebridean was no exception; she
had died beside the hedge, below the willow, which was now
weeping leaves, thin and helpless, in the wind. I examined
both ends of the sheep, as you do, and there was no obvious sign
of disease or illness. The hollow eye cavity stared dully at the
sky. The coroner's verdict as to cause of death? One of those
things.

Or even age. She was ten, was Bess. There were grey hairs in her coat and around her muzzle. She was an old lady.

~

Pro-environment uses of a sheep, Number 29:

This is a story of sheep and April flowers.

A field we rent is in a wood, all by itself. It is a place at once curious and lovely. When you think 'field', you think of England's familiar open patchwork landscape, where fields adjoin each other, separated by hedge or stock fence. But England's first fields were hacked from the wildwood by the Stone Agers wherever was easy, such as a pre-existing glade. Agriculture was not a continuous creeping frontier, but done here and there, in bits and pieces. Our first farmland was inside woodland. Like Mr Geary's field.

Going into Mr Geary's field, then, is to take a long step back in time. That is why his square, three-acre paddock is odd. The beauty of the place is its birdsong, especially on a light, airy April evening like this. The birds perform evensong on all sides, to make four walls of sound.

Anyway, to the flowers. When we took over the rental two years ago, Mr Geary apologized for the field's state, saying, 'It is a bit overgrown.' Having moved to the Big Smoke decades ago, he keeps the field as a remote souvenir of his roots. True enough, without husbandry, the field had gone rampant to moss and ryegrass, and little but. Brambles from the wood had extended their tentacles ten yards in. There were assertive little sprigs of oaks everywhere.

Trees are good, yet they would take over and reforest the world if they could. Bring everything under their shadow. We need pastureland.

Mr Geary dropped a heavy hint. 'Of course, it would be wonderful to have some meadow flowers in there, like there used to be.' So, for the last two years I have been planting wild-flowers and stemming the bramble and oak invasion. (I say 'I' but some of the graft has been done by the teeth of cattle and sheep, as well as the whirling steel blades of motorized scythes and flail-cutters.)

The aim is not a 'wildflower meadow', or a traditional hay-field. But rough grazing with some floral richness. A bit of colour amid the tussocks.

Altruism, and a feeling for Nature, are among my motives. Another is practical, hard-headed, to be put on the plus-side of the financial balance sheet. Botanical diversity in the sward is good for the health of the stock. As the old farming saw has it, 'Livestock make meadows, meadows make livestock.'

The meat the sheep and I make together is made of grass, and flowers, and herbs.

~

Pro-environment uses of a sheep, Number 30:

My mother, as a child, remembered shoddy being dug into the hopyards of Woodston Farm outside Tenbury Wells, where her father was manager. 'Shoddy' was wool bits left over from the manufacture of carpets in nearby Kidderminster. About five tons of shoddy was applied on the yards – as we from Herefordshire and Worcestershire call 'hop gardens' – each January.

Wool is a natural fertilizer, rich in nitrogen and potassium. (Mineral content overall 10–12 per cent.) Courtesy of my mother's knowledge, I began applying the 'daggings', the bits cut off the rear end of the sheep when tidying them up, to the garden. I then progressed to spreading the daggings over larger areas under cultivation.

I told people. People then wanted to buy whole fleeces as fertilizer. So even the worst fleeces have value.

~

Pro-environment uses of a sheep, Number 31:

We need to insulate above the kitchen. We will use the best insulation material. Sheep's wool.

~

Pro-human uses of sheep (lost count):

In 2006 I shared jury duty at Hereford County Court with Juliet Noble who, with Martin Orbach, made ice cream from sheep's milk, sold primarily through Shepherd's Parlour in Hay-on-Wye.

I love this ice cream. My entire family love it. Thousands of people who descend on the border town for the Hay Literary Festival love it.

But then you think, Where is Britain's sheep's *cheese*? The French have Roquefort, Abbaye de Bellocq, Brique, Berger de Rocastin, Agour, Ossau-Iraty, Fleur de Maquis . . .

The Greeks have Feta and Halloumi.

And so on, nation upon nation.

Originally made from Cheviots' milk in the Scottish Borders, sheep's cheese in Britain seems to have died out in the nineteenth century. After 1933 and the establishment of the Milk Marketing Board, which guaranteed a minimum price for dairy milk, the milking of everything but cows was finished.

~

Pro-environment uses of a sheep, Number 32:

November: left to their own devices, ponds dry up through the process of succession, filling with vegetation and becoming overgrown by darkening bankside plants. This morning, with wind taking my breath away, I put the Hebrideans in to graze the sedge (*Carex riparia*) overcrowding the edge of the farm pond. With their mouth shears, the sheep will save the pond from being smothered to death.

~

Recently, I read the 'how to' manual of a fourteenth-century French shepherd, Jean de Brie. Shepherding was a career he took pride in, noting how Biblical characters such as Moses and David were also shepherds, and that 'numberless people take their living, food, and support, for the most part, from the profit and gain of sheep'. *Plus ça change.*

What has changed is human respect for sheep. It has reversed. Here is de Brie on the correct attitude to ovines:

First of all, the lambs, young and tender, should be treated kindly and without violence and should not be struck or corrected with switches, sticks or whips nor any other kind of beating that could hurt or bruise them, for they would fall off and become thin and weak. Rather one should lead them gently and kindly by leadership and correction.

On shearing:

In May the weather is fair and calm and not yet too hot. Everything on earth is in full flower, for then she has put on her beautiful gown, adorned with many lovely little flowers of diverse colors, in woods and meadows – it is then that the pastures are filled with beautiful, tender plants. In May it is the custom to shear the wool from rams, ewes, yearlings, and lambs, since the wool is ready then. It is also more appropriate and greatly profitable to shear the sheep then than at any other time, as much for the season's moderate heat as for ease in pasturing.

Of himself as shepherd:

From experience which is the greatest teacher, I learned through great application the theory, practice, science, and manner of feeding, tending and managing woolbearing animals, and the natural law shown and taught to all animals, not only those who reason, but to all other beasts that are born and live, in the air, on earth, and in the sea.

I made fun of 'Dark Age' veterinary treatments earlier. I have to say, however, that the philosophy of shepherding in the 1300s is superior to that of any 'shepherding' philosophy promoting intensive, indoor sheep farming in the 2000s.

~

Was it Cracker, or was it Crumble? Sometimes, I suspect, my memory is less perfect than that of sheep. Anyway, Shortbread had given birth, a single lamb (the biscuity nomenclature continuing down the generations; we are currently on Bourbon), then she developed mastitis. I did everything you could do, 'stripped out' (milked) the teat of the foul stinking illness, morning in, evening out, dosed her with antibiotics, but it was no use. It rarely is with mastitis.

Anyway, from those last forty-eight hours with Shortbread, a factor in my life and a place in my heart for a decade, some thoughts . . .

I love cattle and pigs, I have a deep affection for chickens and geese, but sheep are special. It's there in the Bible. Jesus is the 'lamb of God', not His calf, His piglet, even His kid. I suspect it's the dependency, the fact that sheep require such close care. Humans are hard-wired to want companionship, but also to protect their kith, kin and charges. Sheep, especially their gentle offspring, fit the bill like no other farmyard animal.

I am not pretending to nobility. Being a shepherd has entirely selfish aspects; there's a romance to shepherding which is entirely absent from pig and poultry farming. In a time of technology, in a time of cities and disconnect from the countryside, shepherds, male or female, feel themselves to be the last of a breed: hard, solitary individuals doing real graft out in the elements. It's almost heroic.

But not as heroic as Shortbread, quietly and inspirationally suffering the indignity and discomfort of veterinary treatment, and always most anxious about her lamb, rather than herself. Which, of course, is the Christian message, if you think about it.

Shortbread, when it became clear that treatment was failing, was put down. (Cracker or Crumble was brought up thereafter on the bottle.) It may sound trite, but in my eyes Shortbread has never died. I still look out on the fields and see her grazing. And smile to myself.

Curious, too, how even the passing parade of sheep gone by comforts the landscape. Pastoralizes it. Then again, it was sheep, more than any other farm animal, that won the fields and the hills from the wildwood, domesticated the land.

~

14 February, 8 a.m.: I have come in from the cold, opened up the laptop to continue writing this book.

I took a bale of hay down on my shoulder this morning to the Shetlands, to keep the rack topped up. There was a hoar frost last night, and the sun glittered off the field. A few of the sheep were already grazing, and frost beads off the grass had collected in debutantes' necklaces under their chins. I saw that overnight a few of the sheep had nibbled at the thick ivy tendrils in the hedge, back to the white bone, leaving the skin to weep orange at its edges. The hedge is wide and very old; in spring the lambs hide-and-seek inside it; in summer the sheep get up on their back legs to eat the leaves, standing in a line like drinkers at a pub bar.

When they saw me, the Shetlands still lying abed got to their feet and ambled over to meet me at the rack. Where they had been sleeping there were round patches of green, untouched by white, giving that part of the field a pleasant polka-dot effect. An early bird, a blackbird, hopped down from the hedge and began to drill in one of these frost-free places for food.

I broke open the bale, put it in the rack, fluffed it around a bit. The sheep pulled quietly at the blades of dry grass behind the mesh. I stood there next to the rack for about five minutes, with the sheep tight around me, enjoying their company. The scent of the hay and the scent of warm wool filled the frosted air, as it had done for centuries.

## THE SHEPHERD

*How sweet is the shepherd's sweet lot!*
*From the morn to the evening he strays;*
*He shall follow his sheep all the day,*
*And his tongue shall be filled with praise.*
*For he hears the lambs' innocent call,*
*And he hears the ewes' tender reply;*
*He is watchful while they are in peace.*
*For they know when their shepherd is nigh.*

WILLIAM BLAKE,
*Songs of Innocence,* 1789

# APPENDIX

SOME NATIVE BREEDS OF SHEEP, BEING OF
INTEREST TO SHEEP-LOVERS, FARMERS,
CONSERVATIONISTS, LANDOWNERS,
ENVIRONMENTALISTS, KNITTERS, CHEESE-
MAKERS, COUNTRYSIDE-DWELLERS, AND ALL
THOSE INTERESTED IN BRITAIN'S HERITAGE

*1. Soay*

Named after the Hebrides island – *soay* is Norse for 'sheep island' – and the most primitive of our native sheep, hardly different from the little brown horned sheep of Bronze Age farming. Fleet of foot, light-framed, flighty, short-tailed. Their chocolatey wool with white belly closely resembles that of the wild mouflon. Low maintenance – they lose their fleeces naturally, or can be 'rooed' – but have a well-developed escape instinct, and next to no flocking instinct. Ewes weigh around 25kg and rams 40kg. Meat is darker and gamier than most sheep meat. The Soay is generally slaughtered as hogget or mutton as the lambs lack size. A carcase of around 12–13kg can be achieved at a year old.

Wool quality: staple length 5–15cm; Bradford count 44–50; fleece weight 1.5–2.25kg. Used for speciality hand-knitting.

Rare.

*2. North Ronaldsay*

From the same short-tailed northern group as the Soay, Shetland, Hebridean and Manx Loaghtan. A 12-mile-long drystone dyke, built in 1832, on North Ronaldsay keeps these unique seaweed-eating sheep on the shoreline and off farmland. They will swim for the best seaweed, dulse being their favourite. Another quirk is their liking for the meat of dead seabirds. They are poisoned by too much grass. An annual summer festival, www.nrsheepfestival.com, promotes the breed and its meat, usually sold as hogget. Rounding up is known as 'punding'.

Ronaldsay sheep are prolific – three out of four have twins or triplets. Despite this, it is traditional on North Ronaldsay to allow the ewes to keep only one lamb. The crofters prefer wethers (castrated males) because they make bigger carcases.

Rare.

## 3. Boreray

Tough, small breed, able to thrive on sparse grazing. Ewes weigh around 30kg and rams 45kg. Both sexes heavily horned. The breed is long lived, with ewes often lambing into their teens. Average lambing percentage of lowland flocks is around 140 per cent. The breed can shed its fleece, which is usually cream with grey or black and white face and legs, although not all animals do so. The breed originated in the late nineteenth century from a cross between the Blackface and a variety of the old Scottish tan-faced group – of which latter the Boreray is the sole surviving descendant. Still mostly confined to the islands of Scotland; when the inhabitants of St Kilda were evacuated in 1930 the sheep were left on the island of Boreray and have existed as a feral flock ever since. In common with most primitive breeds the Boreray is generally slaughtered as hogget or mutton for a bigger carcase.

Staple length 10–15cm. Fleece weight 1.25kg.

Rare.

## 4. Hebridean

Small, black, horned sheep saved from extinction by aristocrats seeking ornamental parkland animals. The RBST (Rare Breeds Survival Trust: see page 158) formally recognized it in the 1970s and, in 1994, a breed society was started. The sheep have become popular with farmers seeking a fleece as well as a carcase to sell. Widely used for conservation grazing, given its tendency to browse brush and 'weeds', and for the supply of almost jet-black fleece to the home felting and spinning markets. On the sheep's back, the wool greys with age.

Of Iron Age ancestry, the sheep is capable of coping with all weathers, with good mothering instincts, which made it a mainstay of subsistence farming throughout Scotland until the agricultural revolutions in the eighteenth century. The black colouring is recessive, but once selected and bred for, it sticks. Celtic peoples liked the black colouring and not just because of the colour – black horned feet are tougher.

Some Hebrideans are double-coated, and like their Shetland relatives may have a very soft downy undercoat. Fleeces range from 1.4–3.6kg (3–8lb) with a wildly varying staple length. Micron count is generally coarse, around 33–38.

Traditional.

## 5. Manx Loaghtan

This is the Isle of Man's sheep, related to the Soay and Hebridean. 'Loaghtan' derives from *lugh dhoan*, which is Manx for mouse brown or 'moorit' (see Castlemilk Moorit). Hugely horned: rams can have six of them. Lamb has EU Protected Designation of Origin (PDO) status. It is distinguished by the rich brown colour of the fleece. Proven to be naturally resistant to gastrointestinal worms. Ewes can produce lambs at up to 13–14 years old. Depending on management, lambing percentages between 130 and 170 can be expected. Ewes weigh around 40kg and rams 55kg. An active browser, thus good for conservation grazing. The Manx fleece is exceptionally hard-wearing.

Staple length 8–13cm. Fleece weight 1.5kg. Quality 44s–48s. Meat usually sold as hogget or mutton.

Rare.

## 6. *Castlemilk Moorit*

Sir Jock Buchanan-Jardine bred this dainty, gazelle-like sheep to adorn the parkland of his Castlemilk estate in Dumfriesshire, and clothe his workers, in the early part of the twentieth century. The breed is composed of part Manx Loaghtan, mouflon and *moorit* (lowland Scots for 'chocolate-coloured') Shetland to make a milk-coffee brown, pale-bellied sheep, with discernible white mouflon 'spectacles'. After Sir Jock's death, RBST founder the late Joe Henson kept the breed going at his Cotswold Farm Park. With good management a lambing percentage of around 160 to 170 can be achieved. Rams and ewes horned. Ewes weigh around 40kg and rams 55kg. The fleece has little or no kemp and is highly prized by hand-spinners.

Staple length 4–7cm. Fleece weight 1kg. Quality 48s–50s. Pure-bred sheep are slow to mature but as shearlings produce a flavoursome, quality, fine-grained lean meat.

Rare.

## 7. *Balwen*

Balwen, which means 'white blaze' in Welsh, is arguably the handsomest of the Welsh hill breeds, with its uniform facial marking, four white socks (mandatory in males) and white-tipped long tail akin to a fox's brush. As with other colour variations of the Welsh Mountain, the Balwen's coat design made it readily identifiable for farmers seeking their flocks in the big country of mid and west Wales; hails specifically from the Tywi valley in Carmarthenshire and was nearly wiped out by 1947 when there was one sole ram left. Interest since has blossomed, and a breed society was founded in 1985. Relatively docile for a Welsh Mountain-derived breed. Long-lived, with ewes commonly producing lambs at ten years plus. Rams are horned, ewes are polled.

Rare.

## 8. Dorset Horn

Pass a Young's pub, and you will teach yourself to recognize a Dorset Horn: the brewery has adopted the breed as its logo. The Dorset has a distinctive pink nose, white face, creamy fleece, and both sexes are horned, the rams with large, crazy spiral affairs. Docile, and capable of lambing the year round, the breed probably developed from crossing the tan-faced sheep of Dorset with a merino-type breed. Ewes can produce lambs at up to 10–12 years old. Lambing percentages vary between 140 and 200, depending on management. Now a rare breed, despite once being a popular export to Australasia, North America and South Africa. Pure-bred lambs are often killed from 10 weeks to give a 16–20+kg carcase.

Staple length 8–10cm. Fleece weight 2.25–3kg. Quality 54s–58s.

Traditional.

## 9. Badger Face

Ancient Welsh Mountain breed, which comes in two colour schemes: the more usual Torddu (pronounced 'torthee'), meaning 'black belly', is a white sheep with black eye stripes and a black underbelly that stretches up to the jaw; the less common Torwen, 'white belly', has the reverse colour scheme, a black sheep with a white belly and small white eye patches. Both parents need to carry the badger-face gene for the lamb to have the markings.

Of ancient lineage. The old alternative name for Torddu – Defaid Idloes – is that of a seventh-century Welsh saint, Idloes.

Traditional.

## 10. Llanwenog

Black-faced, black-legged cross between the local primitive Cardy and Shropshire Down, brought into mid Wales when the railways first penetrated there in 1867. Its heartland is, as the name indicates, Llanwenog in the Teifi valley of west Wales. Famously prolific: lambing percentage of 230 – for the flock – is not unknown. Lambs are small, ewes lamb easily. Ewes weigh around 55–60kg and rams 80–90kg. Head and ears are black, and both ewes and rams are polled. For a time, the Llanwenogs were called many names, from Blackface to Shropshire Crosses, but the breed was finally named Llanwenog in 1957.

Traditional.

## 11. Lleyn

Bakewell is responsible for this stolid, solid white sheep from north-west Wales. He sent his Dishley Leicester rams to improve Irish ewes in County Roscommon and the results were imported into Wales in the nineteenth century by Lloyd Edwards of Nanhoron and Lord Mostyn of the Lleyn peninsula. In 1970, when the dwindling breed was on last hooves, Moses Griffith called a meeting in Pwllheli to rekindle interest; a society was formed. The Lleyn now flourishes; Prince Charles has a flock at Highgrove.

Traditional.

## 12. Wensleydale

With its long, lustrous, purled fleece, could pass for a Suzuki hound. The forelock ('topping') was grown so judges could determine fleece quality. Originated in North Yorkshire in the 1840s when Bluecap, a Dishley Leicester ram born in 1839, was crossed with a Teeswater ewe.

The fleece is kemp-free and Wensleydale wool is used for its special effects in hand-knitting yarn, knitwear and cloth, and sometimes in upholstery fabrics. Due to its similarity to mohair, regularly blended with same. Colours span black to silver grey.

Staple length 20–30cm. Bradford count 44–48. Micron measurement 33–35. Fleece weight 6–9kg.

Traditional.

## 13. Herdwick

A Lake District icon. 'Herdwyck' is an ancient Norse word for sheep pasture. A hardy, dual-purpose (meat and fleece) sheep, which has a strong hefting tendency. Body is ursine, coat hoar-white on face, steel grey on flanks and back when mature (lambs are born black, then go brown before becoming shearlings). As with some other primitive sheep, there are two coats: a woolly waistcoat and a hairy outer. The wool is coarse and difficult to dye; it's also an excellent insulator, so can be found in fireproofed sheets of loft insulation. Since 2013 Herdwick meat has EU Protected Designation of Origin (PDO) status.

National Trust founder Canon Hardwicke Rawnsley was instrumental in formalizing the breed and inspired Beatrix Potter to keep them; her will stipulated that Herdwicks should remain on her land. Beatrix Potter's longest story, *The Fairy Caravan*, featured her own Herdwick sheep. Today, around 99 per cent of Herdwick sheep are kept in commercial flocks in the central and western dales of the Lake District, with 95 per cent within 14 miles of Coniston.

The instinct for Herdwicks to remain on the 'heaf' (heft) on which they were born is strong; there are tales of draft Herdwick ewes being sold in the autumn sales in Broughton-in-Furness in the far south of the Lake District only to appear at their home heaf at spring gather in late March, having travelled 40 or 50 miles to get there.

Unusually for the UK, Herdwick were the subject of transhumance, the seasonal walking of sheep from winter quarters to summer grazing and back. Traditionally, young Herdwicks from the northern parts of Lakeland were walked to the mild coastal marshes on the Solway, where they would spend the five months from 1 November to 1 April, just as the older sheep were being brought down to the enclosed fields around the farm for lambing.

Herdwick fleece was used to weave Hodden Grey, a coarse, undyed cloth made by, among others, John Woodcock Graves of Caldbeck, the man who composed 'D'ye ken John Peel' about his hunting friend of that name. Peel's 'coat so grey' was Hodden, as was the tartan of the London Scottish Regiment, for whom the Hodden's monochrome obviated inter-clan rivalry but did offer camouflage in the field.

Traditional.

## 14. Border Leicester

Known as the Great Improver, Britain's largest indigenous sheep, with its distinctive prick ears and Roman nose, is descended from Bakewell's famous Dishley Leicesters. Once the most sought-after sheep in the world for cross-breeding. However, it's now classified as 'at risk' by the RBST, and its close relation, the Bluefaced Leicester, is far more common.

From the Scottish rather than Welsh borders, the breed is renowned for its docility and good maternal qualities. Lambing percentages vary between 165 and 180. Ewes weigh around 80–100kg and rams 120–145kg. The fleece of rams weighs 6–9kg, ewes 4–6kg, with a grade of 48–50 Bradford (29–32 microns), and is sought after by hand-spinners for its natural lustre and ability to take dye. The wool quality is conferred to crosses.

Rare.

## 15. Suffolk

Ubiquitous, black-faced sheep (with endearing floppy ears), developed around rotational farming – summer clover, winter turnips and the salt marshes – in the eighteenth century by crossing

Norfolk Horn ewes with Southdown rams in the Bury St Edmunds area. News of its superiority spread quickly – in 1797, farming commentator Arthur Young stated in his review of the county's agriculture: 'These ought to be called the Suffolk breed, the mutton has superior texture, flavour, quantity and colour of gravy.' It's now the top-ranking British breed, its bloodlines found all over the world from Russia to South America. Has some character, unlike such competitors as Texel, and boasts elegant black legs. A big presence in the field. Full-size adult Suffolk rams 113–159kg, ewes 81–113kg.

In 2011 at Stirling, a buyer from north Wales bought a Suffolk ram lamb, born 3 January 2011, for 90,000 guineas. A codicil is that Suffolks are inherently susceptible to scrapie.

Traditional/commercial.

## 16. Cotswold

Probably brought over by the Romans, and in such demand with foreign merchants that Henry VI licensed their export and the fleeces of no other. Numbers plummeted dramatically with the drop in the wool trade; by the mid-twentieth century there was just one large breeding flock. Since 1966, the efforts of hobby farmers, plus breeder William Garne of Aldsworth, have brought about a resurgence. The breed appears to have been given the name 'Cotswold' because they were housed in shelters known as 'cots' or 'cotes' and pastured on the wild, treeless hills of the area called 'wolds'.

Lambing percentage is generally 150 to 175. Lambs are large but the breed has few lambing problems and lambs rise and suckle quickly. Ewes are very milky and excellent mothers. A long tall sheep; ewes weigh around 85–90kg and rams 130kg. The breed has a well-developed forelock to distinguish Cotswolds from other longwool breeds. Unsurprisingly, the heavy, lustrous wool is much in demand with hand-spinners.

Staple length 15–20cm. Fleece weight 5.5–10kg. Quality 44s–48s. The breed is suitable for lamb, hogget and mutton production but can go to fat.

Rare.

## 17. Portland

The insularity of life on this barren island off the Dorset coast helped preserve the characteristics of this small, hardy, downland sheep, with its tan face (framed by horns) and matching legs. Unlike other primitive UK breeds, the Portland is probably of Mediterranean origin, hence the tendency to spring just one lamb per season. There were some 4,000 sheep on the island in 1840, but improved connections with the mainland resulted in the breed being swamped by competition. (There were always Portlands at Calke Abbey in Derbyshire, however, where a flock had been established in 1770.) Rescued from near extinction thanks to the RBST.

Lambs are born a russet-red colour. This fades into creamy brown as the sheep ages. Ewes weigh 35–40kg and rams around 55kg. The Portland will eat rough grasses and browse on shrubs so is a good choice for certain conservation grazing situations. The Portland is usually taken to hogget and mutton as the lambs lack size. The meat is known for its flavour; George III was a fan.

Staple length 6–9cm. Fleece weight 2–3kg. Quality 50s–60s.

Rare.

## 18. Devon and Cornwall Longwool

Comically curly, laidback breed, reputed to produce more wool per sheep than any other British breed – even the lambs can be sheared. An amalgam of the South Devon and Devon Longwool; the flock book was established in 1977. The hard-wearing wool is chiefly used in carpets, as well as for dolls' hair and needle felting. The breed remains lean and is suitable for taking to hogget and mutton. Both sexes are polled.

Staple length 20–25cm. Fleece weight 7–10kg. (Some examples have weighed 20kg.)

Rare.

### 19. Derbyshire Gritstone

One of the oldest native sheep breeds in Britain, originating in the Peak District around 1770, and with its black-and-white face and legs, one of the prettiest. But no weakling; strong, resistant to weather and disease; ewes weigh 55–65kg, rams 80–100kg. Wool is of a very high quality, with an excellent staple, free from 'kemp' and possessing crimp; while most hill breed wool goes to carpets, the fine fleece of the Derbyshire Gritstone is woven into knitwear, worsted and hosiery.

Rare.

### 20. Shetland

Small fine-boned sheep of the Northern Short-tailed group, closely related to the now extinct Scottish Dunface. By the early twentieth century, the Shetland itself was threatened by cross-breeding. A protective, energetic Shetland Flock Book Society was formed in 1927. Farmed mainly today for its very fine wool, which comes in a useful range of colours and patterns (saves dyeing), these usually referred to by dialect Shetland names, among them *musket* (light greyish-brown), *shaela* (dark steely-grey), *moorit* (reddish brown), *mioget* (honey-toned, yellowish-brown), *katmoget* ('badger-face': dark belly and dark shading around nose and eyes, lighter elsewhere), *yuglet* (generally light with dark 'panda' patches around the eyes), *bleset* (dark with white blaze down face). Tweed is produced from the coarser Shetland wool, but the Isles are best known for their multi-coloured knitwear (made using Fair Isle knitting). Fleeces usually weigh 2–4lb (0.9–1.8kg). In November 2011, Shetland wool produced in the Shetlands gained PDO classification as 'Native Shetland Wool'. It was the first non-food product in the UK to receive this status. The UK population of registered breeding ewes is over 3,000. Rams weigh 41–57kg and ewes 34–45kg.

Traditional.

### 21. Teeswater

County Durham sheep with a lineage stretching back two hundred years. Large, hornless, producing a fine, long-stapled lustre wool with a natural permanent curl and with no dark fibres in the fleece. A fleece from the first clip can weigh up to 8kg with a staple length of 30cm. Teeswater wool is in demand for worsted suiting, knitting wools, and also blending with other fibres.

Traditional.

### 22. Lincoln

Between the 1850s and the 1920s, when the Lincoln was still a force in the land, many thousands were exported for cross-breeding to create the sheep of the New World. In New Zealand, the Lincoln went on to create the Polwarth, a dual-purpose wool and meat breed, one-quarter Lincoln and three-quarters Spanish merino, and the Corriedale, one-quarter merino and three-quarters Lincoln. There are now estimated to be one hundred million of these two breeds grazing the southern hemisphere.

But by 1971 fewer than five hundred breeding Lincoln ewes remained in the UK, in fifteen small flocks. Numbers increased a little in the 1980s and have stabilized at about seven hundred. Mature ewes weigh 90–113kg. Lincolns are rectangular in form, deep-bodied and wide. Vies with the Cotswold to produce the heaviest fleece: a 27-month-old ram produced, in 2005, a fleece of 47.5lb (21.5kg).

Rare.

## 23. Jacob

Old, unimproved piebald breed, carrying two, four, sometimes six horns. (The multiple horns can lead to split-eyelid.)

They only look like white sheep with black spots; they are actually black sheep with white blotches. Black on fleece fades to grey with age. Origins obscure; quite possibly from the Holy Land as per the Bible. One legend attributes its presence in the UK to escaped ovines from the Spanish Armada. Then again, such happenstance is said to explain the arrival in the isles of several other breeds. As *Country Life* pointed out in 1953, 'one begins to wonder if Noah had not passed by [Britain's coast] in his Ark'.

A majestic sheep that improves any landscape you put it in. Wool popular with hand-spinners. Typical fleeces weigh 2–2.5kg (5lb) and vary in colouring, crimp and fineness. Staple length 8–17cm. Bradford count 44–56. Micron measurement 28–39.

Traditional.

## 24. Leicester Longwool

Hugely important breed in the history of livestock development. In the first half of the eighteenth century the longwool breeds of the Midlands were large and slow-growing with a poor carcase. Robert Bakewell took the example of the Leicester breed and by crossing it with the Lincoln and Ryeland breeds was able to create the New Leicester. Although the objective was breed improvement, the New Leicester had several faults and never dominated the industry. William Youatt eulogized:

> The New Leicester, is the most valuable of long-woolled sheep. As a lowland sheep, and destined to live on good pasture, the New Leicester is without a rival – in fact he has improved, if he has not given the principal value to all the other long-woolled sheep. The head should be hornless; the eyes prominent, but with a quiet expression; the ears thin, long, and directed

backward. The neck full and broad at its base, and gradually tapering to the head; the breast broad and full; the shoulders broad and round: the arm fleshy through its whole extent, and even down to the knee; the bones of the leg small, standing wide apart; no looseness of skin about them, and comparatively bare of wool. The quarters long and full; the thighs also wide and full. The legs of a moderate length; the pelt moderately thin, but soft and elastic, and covered with a good quantity of white wool, not so long as in some breeds, but considerably finer. This account combines the main excellences of both Bakewell's own breed, and Culley's variety or improvement of it. It is precisely the form for a sheep provided with plenty of good food, and without any great distance to travel, or exertion to make in gathering it. The principal recommendations of this breed, are its beauty and fulness of form, comprising in the same apparent dimensions, greater weight than any other sheep; an early maturity, and a propensity to fatten, equalled by no other breed; a diminution in the proportion of offal, and the return of most money for the quantity of food consumed.

In time the name of the breed was changed to the Leicester Longwool and the Breed Society was formed in 1893. A very tall, long-legged breed with a characteristic longwool fleece. Ewes weigh around 80–100kg and rams 100–150kg. Animals have woolless white faces and legs, and both sexes are polled. Docile but requires muscles. There is also a black strain of the breed. The wool is popular with hand-spinners and well suited to direct marketing of woollen products. Staple length 20–25cm. Fleece weight 5–7.5kg. Quality 40s–46s.

## 25. *Whitefaced Woodland*

In part a misnamed breed, the face is indeed white but the sheep has nothing to do with trees, originating in the Pennine hills on the borders of Derbyshire and Yorkshire. The Cheviot and the merino were utilized in the breed's development. One of the stockiest hill breeds: ewes weigh around 60–70kg and rams can reach 130kg. Both sexes are horned, with rams having heavy spiralled 'handlebars'. The breed is now popular with commercial farmers, smallholders and those requiring conservation grazing, being an unfussy eater and eligible for environmental and countryside stewardship subsidies. The pure-bred Whitefaced Woodland lamb will reach a deadweight of 18–20kg within five months, and is still lean well into hogget age. Ewes can produce lambs into their teens and lambing percentages are up to 150 on the hill. An alternative name for the breed is the Penistone after the town that has held a sheep fair since 1699.

Approximate staple length 15cm. Fleece weight 2–3kg. Quality 44s–50s.

Rare.

## 26. *Hill Radnor*

As the name suggests, this hill breed hails from the Radnor Hills of the Welsh Borders, which was almost its undoing, since the area was particularly affected by the Foot-and-Mouth cull of 2001. The sheep is probably typical of the old Welsh tan-faced sheep that used to roam the area; reference was being made to the breed as far back as 1911 and a Breed Society was formed in 1949. A hill breed but bulkier than a Welsh Mountain, and thankfully easy-going. Ewes weigh around 50–55kg and rams 70–80kg. Thick white fleece, tan face, aquiline nose. Ewes are polled, rams are horned. Pure-bred Hill Radnor lamb can reach around 17kg at eight weeks of age and will be ready to kill at 4–5 months.

Staple length 8–10cm. Fleece weight 2–2.5kg. Quality 48s–56s. Rare.

### 27. Cheviot

Northerly representative of a dun-faced sheep kept by the Celtic peoples long before the Romans came. Native to the Scottish Borders and Northumbria. Lively, attractive (prick ears), white-faced, hornless, longwoolled, and capable of standing almost anything the elements can throw at it. Like the Herdwick, a breed moved between winter and summer grazing (transhumance); during the winter the sheep grazed the low-lying fields in 'winter town' and in spring were taken uphill to 'spring town'. The ewes were milked in 'yowe buchts' – low, turf-walled enclosures – to make hard cheese ('white meat') for winter.

Cheviot wool has a distinctive helical crimp, which gives it a highly desirable resilience. The fleece is dense and long-stapled, of 50s–56s quality. Bred to look after themselves, Cheviots require little husbandry. Hard black feet make them less prone to foot rot. Their tendency for worm resistance means less drenching, less crutching and less flystrike.

Mature body weight for the rams is 72–90kg with the ewes weighing slightly less at 55–72kg. Mature ewes will average a 2.25–4.5kg fleece that has a micron measurement of 27–33 and a spinning count of 48–56. The staple length of the fleece will be 7.5–12cm with a yield of 50 to 75 per cent.

Traditional.

### Rare Breeds Survival Trust Watchlist (Sheep)

The Rare Breeds Survival Trust is a conservation charity whose purpose is to secure the continued existence and viability of the native farm animal genetic resources (FAnGR) of the United Kingdom. It was founded in 1973 by Joe Henson to preserve native breeds; since then, no UK native breed has become extinct. Tel. 024 7669 6551, email enquiries@rbst.org.uk. This list is based on estimated numbers of registered breeding females producing pure-bred offspring in the UK. The symbol + means increase in numbers; = indicates no change; and − is reduction in breeding stock.

1: CRITICAL (fewer than 150)

2: ENDANGERED (150 to 500)

3: VULNERABLE (500 to 900)
    = Boreray
    − Leicester Longwool
    = Lincoln Longwool
    = North Ronaldsay
    = Whitefaced Woodland
    = Welsh Mountain Pedigree

4: AT RISK (900 to 1500)
    − Balwen
    = Border Leicester
    + Castlemilk Moorit
    − Cotswold
    = Derbyshire Gritstone
    − Devon and Cornwall Longwool
    + Hill Radnor
    − Manx Loaghtan
    + Portland
    = Soay

+ Teeswater
= Wensleydale

5: MINORITY (1500 to 3000)
    = Devon Closewool
    = Dorset Down
    + Dorset Horn
    + Greyface Dartmoor
    = Llanwenog
    – Norfolk Horn
    = Oxford Down

# GLOSSARY

ACCELERATED LAMBING Intensive reproductive management system in which ewes lamb more frequently than once per year, usually three lamb 'crops' every two years. The system requires artificial control of daylight and the administration of hormones, e.g. insertion of vaginal sponges containing progesterone.

BELLWETHER The sheep that leads the flock, often with a bell hanging from its neck.

BOTTLE-LAMB Orphan lamb reared on a bottle of ewe COLOSTRUM and/or ewe-milk replacer. Also pet lamb, poddy lamb, cade lamb, cadie lamb, cosset, dolly, foster lamb, gibby lamb, hobby, suckle lamb, cuckoo lamb, hob, sucklet, meg, tiddler lamb.

BRADFORD COUNT The old measure of the fineness of a fibre of wool (now superseded by the micron). It is based on the number of hanks, 560 yards long, of single-strand wool yarn on a reel that the sorter judged could be spun from a pound of top. A count of 56 meant that the pound of top would make 56 hanks, i.e. 17.8 miles of yarn.

BREAK Thinning of the fleece, producing distinct weakness in one part of the staple.

BREECH BIRTH A birth in which the lamb is presented backwards, with its rear legs tucked under and only its tail presenting.

BROKEN MOUTH A sheep that has lost or broken some of its incisor teeth, usually about six or more years old.

CARDING Turning clean wool from staple to sliver form and separating the fibres.

CAST A sheep that has fallen on to its back and is unable to regain footing without assistance, usually because of pregnancy or a heavy/wet fleece.

CHILVER Ewe lamb before its first shearing (used in the south of England). *See also* GIMMER.

CLEAT The 'interdigital space' in the hoof, containing a sebaceous gland that secretes a thick scented oil to simultaneously prevent chafing and mark territory.

CLIPPING Cutting off the wool. *See also* SHEARING.

COLOSTRUM The first milk a ewe gives after birth. This milk has a high number of antibodies and protects newborn lambs against diseases.

COMBING Straightening long fibres and removing shorter ones with a wire brush.

COMMON GRAZING Common fells are upland areas where sheep flocks from different farms graze freely without fences or walls.

CONDITION SCORING Rating sheep from 1 (lean) to 5 (fat) by handling. For best lambing results, ewes should have a score of about 3.5 when mated.

COWIE Polled ram in the north of England.

CREEP FEEDING Providing supplemental feed to lambs.

CRIMP The natural folding and curling of wool fibre.

CROSS-BREED Sheep that are a combination of two or more different breeds. This can make them stronger (hybrid vigour) for a certain environment and in some cases more disease resistant.

CRUTCHING (or CROTCHING) Shearing wool from the hind end of the sheep, usually to prevent FLYSTRIKE. May also be done pre-tupping on both ewes and rams. *See also* DAGGING.

CULL EWES Ewes that have reached the end of their breeding life and are sold for meat.

DAGGING As with CRUTCHING, clipping away wool around a sheep's rear that is soiled, or might become soiled, with urine or faeces, to discourage FLYSTRIKE.

DAGS Lumps of dung, usually in a teardrop shape, stuck to the wool around the sheep's tail and anus. Dags may lead to FLYSTRIKE.

DINMONT A neutered ram, between one and two years of age, in the north of England and southern Scotland.

DIPPING Immersing sheep completely in a chemical wash to kill external parasites. Now largely replaced with the use of POUR-ONS and injectable insecticides.

DOWN BREEDS Breeds created as short-wool terminal sires for meat production. All descend ultimately, in part at least, from John Ellman's improved Southdown.

DRAFT EWE Older female sheep from a hill farm that has been 'drafted' or drawn out from the flock for sale. Usually the ewe will go for further breeding with a longwool on a lowland farm to produce hybrid breeding females.

DRENCH Veterinary medicine administered orally, usually by a drenching gun.

DRIVING (or DROVING) Walking animals from one place to another.

EAR TAG Metal or plastic tag clipped permanently in the ear, carrying ID text or an electronic chip. Obligatory by law. *See also* LUG MARK.

EWE A female sheep that has had her first lamb. In some areas 'yow'.

F1 GENERATION First 'filial generation', i.e. the first cross between two different pure breeds.

FLEECE The wool from a single sheep in the shorn state.

FLUSHING (sheep) Providing improved nutrition in the few weeks before mating to improve fertility, or in the period before birth to increase lamb birth-weight.

FLUSHING (eggs/embryo) Removing unfertilized or fertilized egg from an animal; often as part of an embryo transfer procedure.

FLYSTRIKE Infestation of wool, skin and eventually flesh by the maggots of the blowfly.

FOLD Place where sheep are gathered behind fencing or walls, either for their protection or to manure ground.

FOOT ROT Infectious pododermatitis, a painful hoof disease of sheep (also goats and cattle), especially when pastured on damp ground.

GELD/GELT An adult ewe that is not in lamb when others are. Barren.

GESTATION PERIOD Length of pregnancy. In sheep, 147 days on average.

GIMMER A female sheep that has been weaned but not yet sheared, especially in the north of England and Scotland. Usually around 6 to 15 months old. *See also* THEAVE and CHILVER.

GRADING Assessing, by eye and touch, a fleece's type and quality.

GRAFT The act of transferring a lamb to a ewe that is not its mother, also known as mothering on.

GREASY Wool that has been shorn but still contains lanolin.

GUMMER A sheep that has lost all of its teeth in old age.

HANK Loose skein of wool 560 yards long.

HEFT Area of hillside or open land where a sheep stays instinctively, without fencing. The instinct is passed from generation to generation. Also known as 'heath' and 'heaf'.

HOGG (or HOGGET) A young sheep of either sex from the January after its birth until it cuts two permanent incisor teeth at about 18 months old and/or its first shearing. In former times, hogget also referred to meat of young sheep.

HOOF SHEARS Tool for trimming hooves, similar to secateurs.

IN LAMB Pregnant.

JUG A pen used for keeping a ewe and her newborn lambs so that they can bond.

KED *Melophagus ovinus*, a wingless fly that is a parasite for sheep.

KEMP Short, coarse, hairy fibres in the fleece that are not wool.

LAMB A sheep in its first year up to weaning, generally at six months, or the meat thereof. The main cuts of the latter are: scrag end (of neck), middle neck, best end (of neck), loin, chump (and chump chops), leg (gigot in Scotland), shank, shoulder, breast.

LAMBING The birth process of sheep, the work of tending lambing ewes.

LAMBING PEN A small pen used to keep a ewe and her newborns together, promoting bonding.

LAMBING PERCENTAGE The number of lambs successfully reared in a flock compared to the number of ewes who mated. This is a consideration of lamb and ewe mortality rates, not a comparison of the number of ewes giving birth versus the number of lambs born. May vary from around 100 per cent in a hardy mountain flock (where a ewe may not be able to rear more than one lamb safely), to 150 per cent or more in a well-fed lowland flock (whose ewes can more easily support twins or even triplets).

LAMLAC Dry powdered ewe-milk replacer, the first such commercially available in the UK. Used in bottle or feeding machines.

LANOLIN Thick, yellow, fatty oil found in sheep's wool. This is secreted by the sheep's skin to allow water resistance, and can be extracted for use in a number of industries, including cosmetics. This is also known as wool fat, wool grease, wool wax or yolk.

LUG MARK Local term in Cumbria for EAR TAG.

LUSTRE The degree to which wool fibre will reflect light and 'sheen'. Longwools such as Wensleydale, Greyfaced Leicester and Cotswold have high lustre. Such wool dyes effectively.

MICRON Measure of wool-fibre diameter. 1 micron is 0.001mm. The lower the micron figure, the finer the quality.

MOB A group of sheep run together for grazing purposes.

MONORCHID Male mammal with only one descended testicle and one retained internally. If a sheep, also called a rig.

MOORIT Chocolate brown wool.

MULE Type of crossbred ewe, usually a cross between a hill-breed ewe and a Border or Bluefaced Leicester tup. May be called a Scotch Mule (from a Blackface ewe) or Welsh Mule (from a Welsh Mountain ewe), or other geographical term. Usually put to a TERMINAL SIRE to produce fat lambs.

MUTTON Meat from an older sheep, slowly regaining popularity because of its flavour.

NOIL Short fibre removed during combing.

NOTIFIABLE DISEASE One that, by law, livestock keepers are obliged to bring immediately to the attention of Animal Health. Foot-and-Mouth, for example.

ORF Contagious ecthyma, a highly contagious viral disease of sheep (and goats) attacking damaged skin areas around the mouth and causing sores, usually affecting lambs in their first year of life.

OVER-WINTERING When sheep are sent from upland areas of Britain to warmer lowland areas where feed is more easily available over the winter.

OVINE Relating to sheep.

PELT The skin of a (dead) sheep with the wool on.

POLLED Hornless.

POUR-ON Medicine applied along the backline to prevent external parasites. Spot-ons are similar but are applied as a spot on the back of the neck.

RADDLE Coloured paint applied to a ram's chest (usually in the form of a 'crayon' held in a harness) that will mark a ewe's rump when serviced by the ram. This lets the farmer know which ewes have not yet mated and should remain longer with the ram. *See also* RUDD.

RAM An uncastrated male sheep. Also TUP.

RAM EFFECT Describes the effect of stimulating ewes to ovulate by introducing a ram or teaser ram.

RAW WOOL Wool from the sheep's back, still containing dirt and grease.

RIG/RIGWELTED An overturned sheep.

RISE Yellowish line on the sheep's wool caused by the previous winter's greasy wool being lifted away from the skin by newer, fresh wool. The rise is a sign that sheep are ready for shearing.

ROOING Removing the fleece by hand-plucking.

RUDD Coloured marking fluid or crayon applied to a ram's chest that will mark a ewe's rump whenever the ram has mounted her.

SALT MARSH LAMB Also known by its French name, *agneau de pré-salé*, it is the meat of sheep grazing on salt marsh in coastal estuaries, which is washed by the tides and supports a range of salt-tolerant grasses and herbs, such as samphire, sparta grass, sorrel and sea lavender. Places where salt marsh lamb are reared in the UK include the Gower Peninsula, Morecambe Bay and the Solway Firth.

SCAB Type of mange in sheep caused by scab mite *Psoroptes ovis*. This is a NOTIFIABLE DISEASE.

SCOURING Washing the wool to remove grease and dirt.

SCOURS Diarrhoea.

SCRAPIE Transmissible Spongiform Encephalopathy or TSE, similar to BSE in cattle. A fatal brain disease.

SCURS Vestigial horns.

SHEARING Cutting off the fleece. *Also* CLIPPING.

SHEARLING A yearling sheep of either sex that has been shorn; thereafter two-shear, three-shear etc.

SHEEPWALK Area of rough grazing occupied by a particular flock or forming part of a particular farm.

SPINNING Pulling out the fibres and adding twist to make a continuous, strong thread.

STAPLE LENGTH The natural length of the fleece fibres.

STONE Weight of 14lb wool, or two 'cloves'. From ancient times wool had its own special weights, which were used well into the last century. The cloves were made from stone (certified as accurate by the Crown) and are the reason that a *stone* is 14lb.

7lb = 1 clove

2 cloves = 1 stone (14lb)

2 stones = 1 tod (28lb)

6½ tods = 1 wey (182lb)

1 woolpack = 240lb (approx.)

2 weys = 1 sack (364lb)

12 sacks = 1 last (approx. 2 tons)

STORE A sheep (usually a weaned lamb) not yet ready for slaughter that is sold for further fattening.

STRIKE *See* FLYSTRIKE.

TEASER A ram that has been vasectomized to make him infertile but is still hormonal. May be run with ewes prior to the 'real' ram being introduced, to bring the ewes into season. *See also* RAM EFFECT.

TEG *See* HOGG.

TERMINAL SIRE A tup, usually a Down breed, used on ewes (usually mules or other cross-breeds) to produce fat lambs for slaughter.

THEAVE Young female sheep, usually before her first lamb (used especially in lowland England). *See also* GIMMER, CHILVER.

TOP KNOT Wool from the forehead or poll of a sheep.

TOPS Wool that has been combed by machine.

TUP (also TIP) An uncastrated male sheep or ram.

VILD In some northern districts, ewes that are barren, or that have weaned their lambs.

WETHER A castrated male sheep.

YOLK *See* LANOLIN.

YOW Local form of EWE.

# BIBLIOGRAPHY

Arnold, G.W. & Pahl, P.J., 'Some aspects of social behaviour in
sheep', *Animal Behaviour*, 22(3), 1974

Arnold, G.W., Wallace, S.R. & Rea, W.A., 'Associations between
individuals and home-range behaviour in natural flocks of three
breeds of domestic sheep', *Applied Animal Ethology*, 7:239, 1974

Barber, E.J.W., *Prehistoric Textiles: The Development of Cloth in
the Neolithic and Bronze Ages with Special Reference to the
Aegean*, Princeton University Press, Princeton, 1991

Bateson, P.P.G., Bateson, P. & Martin, P., *Play, Playfulness,
Creativity and Innovation*, Cambridge University Press,
Cambridge, 2013

Beausoleil, N.J., Blache, D., Stafford, K.J., Mellor, D.J. & Noble,
A.D., 'Selection for temperament in sheep: Domain-general
and context-specific traits', *Applied Animal Behaviour Science*,
139(1–2), 2012

Bensky, M.K., Gosling, S.D. & Sinn, D.L., 'The world from a
dog's point of view: A review and synthesis of dog cognition
research', *Advances in the Study of Behavior*, 45, 2013

Bezzant, John, *Shepherds and Their Dogs*, Merlin Unwin Books,
Ludlow, 2011

Boissy, A. & Dumont, B., 'Interactions between social and
feeding motivations on the grazing behaviour of herbivores:
Sheep more easily split into subgroups with familiar peers',
*Applied Animal Behaviour Science*, 79(3), 233–45, 2002

Boissy, A., Aubert, A., Désiré, L., Greiveldinger, L., Delval, E. &
Veissier, I., 'Cognitive sciences to relate ear postures to
emotions in sheep', *Animal Welfare*, 20(1), 2011

Bremner, K.J., Braggins, J.B. & Kilgour, R., 'Training sheep as "leaders" in abattoirs and farm sheep yards', *Proceedings of the New Zealand Society of Animal Production*, 40, 1980

Broad, K.D., Mimmack, M.L. & Kendrick, K.M., 'Is right hemisphere specialization for face discrimination specific to humans?', *European Journal of Neuroscience*, 12(2), 2000

Carroll, Carleton W. & Hawley Wilson, Lois, *The Medieval Shepherd*, ACRMS Press, Tempe, Arizona, 2012

Davis, H., Norris, C. & Taylor, A., 'Whether ewe know me or not: The discrimination of individual humans by sheep', *Behavioural Processes*, 43(1), 1998

Destrez, A., Deiss, V., Leterrier, C., Boivin, X. & Boissy, A., 'Long-term exposure to unpredictable and uncontrollable aversive events alters fearfulness in sheep', *Animal*, 7(3), 1998

Dodd, C.L., Pitchford, W.S., Edwards, J.E.H. & Hazel, S.J., 'Measures of behavioural reactivity and their relationships with production traits in sheep: A review', *Applied Animal Behaviour Science*, 140(1–2), 2012

Doyle, R.E., Lee, C., Deiss, V., Fisher, A.D., Hinch, G.N. & Boissy, A., 'Measuring judgement bias and emotional reactivity in sheep following long-term exposure to unpredictable and aversive events', *Physiology & Behavior*, 102(5), 2011

Doyle, R.E., Broster, J.C., Barnes, K. & Browne, W.J., 'Temperament, age, and weather predict social interaction in the sheep flock', *Behavioural Processes*, 131, 53–58, 2016

Dumont, B. & Boissy, A., 'Grazing behaviour of sheep in a situation of conflict between feeding and social motivations', *Behavioural Processes*, 49(3), 2000

Dwyer, C., 'The behaviour of sheep and goats' in P. Jensen (Ed.), *The ethology of domestic animals: An introductory text* (pp. 161–76), 2nd edn., CAB International, Wallingford, Oxfordshire, 2009

Dwyer, C.M. & Lawrence, A.B., 'Maternal behaviour in domestic sheep (*Ovis aries*): Constancy and change with maternal experience', *Behaviour*, 137(10), 2000

Dwyer, C.M., McLean, K.A., Deans, L.A., Chirnside, J., Calvert, S.K. & Lawrence, A.B., 'Vocalizations between mother and young in sheep: Effects of breed and maternal experience', *Applied Animal Behaviour Science*, 58(1–2), 1998

Festa-Bianchet, M., 'The social system of sheep; grouping patterns, kinship and female dominance rank', *Animal Behaviour*, 42(1), 1991

Firbank, Thomas, *I Bought a Mountain*, George G. Harrap & Co, London, 1940

Franklin, J.R. & Hutson, G.D., 'Experiments on attracting sheep to move along a laneway: I. Olfactory stimuli', *Applied Animal Ethology*, 8, 1999

Fulkerson, W.J., Adams, N.R. & Gherardi, P.B., 'Ability of castrate male sheep treated with oestrogen or testosterone to induce and detect oestrus in ewes', *Applied Animal Ethology*, 7, 1981

Gossett, A.L.J., *Shepherds of Britain*, Constable & Co., London, 1911

Grubb, P., 'Social organization of Soay sheep and the behaviour of ewes and lambs', in P.A. Jewell, C. Milner & J. Morton Boyd (Eds.), *Island survivors: The ecology of the Soay sheep of St Kilda*, Athlone Press, London, 1974

Hart, Edward, *The Hill Shepherd*, David & Charles, Newton Abbot, 1977

Hersher, L., Richmond, J.B. & Moore, A.U., 'Maternal behavior in sheep and goats', in H.L. Rheingold (Ed.), *Maternal behavior in mammals*, Wiley, New York, 1963

Hild, S., Clark, C.C., Dwyer, C.M., Murrell, J.C., Mendl, M. & Zanella, A.J., 'Ewes are more attentive to their offspring experiencing pain but not stress', *Applied Animal Behaviour Science*, 132, 2011

Jones, J., *The natural history of domestic animals: Containing an account of their habits and instincts, and of the services they render to man*, Charles Scribner's Sons, New York, 1821

Kendrick, K.M., Atkins, K., Hinton, M.R., Broad, K.D., Fabre-Nys, C. & Keverne, E.B., 'Facial and vocal discrimination in sheep', *Animal Behaviour*, 49, 1995

Kendrick, K.M., da Costa, A.P., Leigh, A.E., Hinton, M.R. & Peirce, J.W., 'Sheep don't forget a face', *Nature*, 414, 2001

Kennard, Bob, *Much Ado About Mutton,* Merlin Unwin, 2014

Kilgour, R., 'Design sheep yards to suit the whims of sheep', *N.Z. Farmer*, 98(6), 1977

Launchbaugh, K.L. & Provenza, F.D., 'The effect of flavor concentration and toxin dose on the formation and generalization of flavor aversions in lambs', *Journal of Animal Science*, 72, 1994

Lee, C., Colegate, S. & Fisher, A.D., 'Development of a maze test and its application to assess spatial learning and memory in Merino sheep', *Applied Animal Behaviour Science*, 96(1–2), 2006

Lewis-Stempel, John, *Young Herriot*, BBC Books, London, 2011

Lewis-Stempel, John, 'A compassionate carnivore manifesto', https://unherd.com/2020/06/let-them-eat-mutton-a-compassionate-carnivores-manifesto/

Lewis-Stempel, John, 'What we didn't learn from foot-and-mouth', https://unherd.com/2021/02/foot-and-mouth-taught-us-nothing/

Maina, D. & Katz, L.S., 'Exposure to a recently mated male increases ram sexual performance', *Applied Animal Behaviour Science*, 51(1–2), 1997

Marino, Lori & Merskin, Debra, 'Intelligence, complexity, and individuality in sheep', *Animal Sentience*, 25(1), 2019

Merskin, Debra, *Seeing Species: Re-Presentations of Animals in the Media & Popular Culture*, Peter Lang, Oxford, 2018

Michelena, P., Gautrais, J., Gérard, J.F., Bon, R. & Deneubourg, J.L., 'Social cohesion in groups of sheep: Effect of activity level, sex composition and group size', *Applied Animal Behaviour Science*, 112(1–2), 2008

Morgan, P. D. & Arnold, G. W., 'Behavioural relationships between Merino ewes and lambs during the four weeks after birth', *Animal Production,* 19(2), 1974

Morgan, P.D., Boundy, C.A.P., Arnold, G.W. & Lindsay, D.R., 'The roles played by the senses of the ewe in the location and recognition of lambs', *Applied Animal Ethology*, 1, 1975

Morris, J.E., Fisher, A.D., Doyle, R.E. & Bush, R.D., 'Determination of sheep learning responses to a directional audio cue', *Journal of Applied Animal Welfare Science*, 13(4), 2010

Morton, A.J. & Avanzo, L., 'Executive decision-making in the domestic sheep', *PLoS ONE*, 6(1), 2011

Munro, John H.A., 'Industrial change in the fifteenth- and sixteenth-century low countries: the arrival of Spanish merino wools and the expansion of the "Nouvelles Draperies" ', http://repec.economics.utoronto.ca/files/UT-ECIPA-MUNRO-02-03.pdf

National Sheep Association, *British Sheep*, 9th edn, Malvern, 1998

Nowack, R., 'Senses involved in the discrimination of merino ewes at close contact and from a distance by their newborn lambs', *Animal Behaviour*, 42(3), 1991

Orgeur, P. & Signoret, J. P., 'Sexual play and its functional significance in the domestic sheep (*Ovis ovis L.*)', *Physiology and Behavior*, 33, 1984

Ortman, R., 'Monitoring of oestrus cycles of ewes by ram-seeking behaviour', *Small Ruminant Research*, 37(1/2), 2000

Parrott, R.F., *Physiological responses to isolation in sheep: Social Stress in Domestic Animals*, Kluwer Academic Publishers, Dordrecht, Netherlands, 1990

Piggins, D. & Phillips, C.J.C., 'The eye of the domesticated sheep and its implications for vision', *Journal of Animal Science*, 62(2), 1996

Pollard, J.C. & Littlejohn, R.P., 'Sheltering behaviour and its effects on productivity', *New Zealand Journal of Agricultural Research*, 42(2), 1999

Porter, R.H., Bon, R. & Orgeur, P., 'The role of familiarity in the development of social recognition in lambs', *Behaviour*, 138 (2), 2001

Price, E., Dally, M., Erhard, H., Kelly, M., Moore, N. & Topper, C., 'Manipulating odour cues facilitates add-on fostering in sheep', *Journal of Animal Science*, 76(4), 1998

Power, Eileen, *The Wool Trade in English Medieval History*, 1941, republished in the McMaster University Archive for the History of Economic Thought, http://socserv.mcmaster.ca/econ/ugcm/3ll3/power/WoolTrade.pdf

Rackham, Oliver, *The History of the Countryside*, Dent, London, 1986

Reefmann, N., Kaszàs, F.B., Wechsler, B. & Gygax, L., 'Ear and tail postures as indicators of emotional valence in sheep', *Applied Animal Behaviour Science*, 118(3–4), 2009

Resko, J.A., Perkins, A., Roselli, C.E. & Stormshak, F.K., 'Sexual behaviour of rams: male orientation and its endocrine correlates', *Reproduction in Domestic Animals IV*, Proceedings of the Fifth International Symposium on Reproduction in Domestic Ruminants, Colorado Springs, USA, 1–5 August 1989, 1998

Ritvo, H., 'Learning from animals: Natural history for children in the eighteenth and nineteenth centuries', *Children's Literature*, 13, 1985

Ruiz-de-la-Torre, J.L. & Manteca, X., 'Behavioural effects of social mixing at different stocking densities in sheep', *Animal Welfare*, 8(2), 1999

Ryder, M.L., 'Medieval Sheep and Wool Types', *The Agricultural History Review*, 1984

Sands, Bryony & Wall, Richard, 'Dung beetles reduce livestock gastrointestinal parasite availability on pasture', *Journal of Applied Ecology*, 54, 2017

Savory Institute, 'What Is Holistic Planned Grazing?', https://savory.global

Schreffler, C. & Hohenboken, W.D., 'Dominance and mating behaviour in ram lambs', *Journal of Animal Science*, 39, 1974

Sevi, A., Muscio, A., Dantone, D., Iascone, V. & D'Emilio, F., 'Paddock shape effects on grazing behaviour and efficiency in sheep', *Journal of Range Management*, 54 (2), 2001

Shackleton, D. M. & Shank, C. C., 'A review of the social behavior of feral and wild sheep and goats', *Journal of Animal Science*, 58(2), 1984

Shillito Walser, E., 'Maternal recognition and breed identity in lambs living in a mixed flock of Jacob, Clun Forest and Dalesbred sheep', *Applied Animal Ethology*, 6, 1980

Shillito Walser, E., Hague, P. & Walters, E., 'Vocal recognition of recorded lambs' voices by ewes of three breeds of sheep', *Behaviour*, 78(3–4), 1981

Smith, J.F., 'The influences of the senses of smell, sight and hearing on the sexual behaviour of rams', *Proceedings of the New Zealand Society of Animal Production*, 35, 1975

Squires, V.R. & Daws, G.T., 'Leadership and dominance relationships in Merino and Border Leicester sheep', *Applied Animal Ethology*, 1975

Stolba, A., Lynch, G.N., Hinch, J.J., Adams, D.B., Munro, R.K. & Davies, H.I., 'Social organisation of merino sheep of different ages, sex and family structure', *Applied Animal Behaviour Science*, 27(4), 1990

Sustainable Food Trust, *A Good Life and A Good Death*, 2018
https://sustainablefoodtrust.org/articles/a-good-life-and-a-
good-death-re-localising-farm-animal-slaughter/
Trow-Smith, Robert, *Life from the Land: The Growth of Farming
in Western Europe*, Longmans, London, 1953
Walling, Philip, *Counting Sheep*, Profile Books, London, 2015
Winfield, C.G., Syme, G.J. & Pearson, A.J., 'Effect of familiarity
with each other and breed on the spatial behaviour of sheep in
an open field', *Applied Animal Ethology*, 1981
Yonezawa, T., Sato, K., Uchida, M., Matsuki, N. & Yamazaki,
A., 'Presence of contagious yawning in sheep', *Animal Science
Journal*, 88(1), 2017
Youatt, William, *Sheep: Their Breeds, Management and Diseases*,
Baldwin & Cradock, London, 1837

# ACKNOWLEDGEMENTS

This one is for the sheep. Every day is better because of them. As for the humans, thank you to the following good shepherds, of flocks, life, and books: Penny Lewis-Stempel, Tristram Lewis-Stempel, Freda Lewis-Stempel, Julian Alexander, Ben Clark, Susanna Wadeson, Alex Christofi, Kate Samano, Annette Murphy, Hayley Barnes, Josh Benn, and Beci Kelly.

**John Lewis-Stempel** is a writer and farmer. His books include the *Sunday Times* bestsellers *Woodston*, *The Running Hare* and *The Wood*. He is the only person to have won the Wainwright Prize for Nature Writing twice, with *Meadowland* and *Where Poppies Blow*. In 2016 he was Magazine Columnist of the Year for his column in *Country Life*. He lives in Herefordshire with his wife and two children.